BEES

LECTURES BY
Rudolf Steiner

Translated by Thomas Braatz

Anthroposophic Press

The lectures in this book were translated from German by Thomas Braatz. The Prelude is an excerpt from lecture 17 in the *Collected Works of Rudolf Steiner*, volume 348, *Über Gesundheit und Krankheit Grundlagen einer geisteswissenschaftlichen Sinneslehre*, published by Rudolf Steiner Verlag, Dornach, Switzerland, 1981. The remaining eight lectures are from volume 351, *Mensch und Welt Das Wirken des Geistes in der Natur Über die Bienen*, published by Rudolf Steiner Verlag, Dornach, Switzerland, 1966. Blackboard drawings were added as an insert in the 1988 German edition.

Translation copyright © Anthroposophic Press, 1998. Introduction copyright © Gunther Hauk, 1998. Afterword copyright © David Adams, 1998.

Published by Anthroposophic Press

www.steinerbooks.org

Library of Congress Cataloging-in-Publication Data

Steiner, Rudolf, 1861–1925.
   [Über die Bienen. English]
   Bees / Rudolf Steiner.
      p. cm.
   Includes index.
   ISBN 0-88010-457-0 (pbk.)
     1. Anthroposophy. 2. Bees—Miscellanea. I. Title.
   BP595.S894U2313 1998
   299.935—dc21   98-6452
                              CIP

Page 189: "Bienenkönigin (für Bronze)," 1958, goldbronze 14.4 x 9.5 cm, by Joseph Beuys, © 1998 Artists Rights Society (ARS), New York/VG Bild-Kunst, Bonn. Photograph: courtesy of Oeffentliche Kunstsammlung Basel, Kupferstichkabinett. Photocredit: Oeffentliche Kunstsammlung Basel, Martin Bühler.

10 9 8

• Contents

Introduction by Gunther Hauk   *vii*

Prelude
Dornach, February 3, 1923   *1*

Lecture 1
Dornach, November 26, 1923   *5*

Lecture 2
Dornach, November 28, 1923   *24*

Lecture 3
Dornach, December 1, 1923   *40*

Lecture 4
Dornach, December 5, 1923   *65*

Lecture 5
Dornach, December 10, 1923   *83*

Lecture 6
Dornach, December 12, 1923   *103*

Lecture 7
Dornach, December 15, 1923   *120*

Lecture 8
Dornach, December 22, 1923   *140*

Blackboard Drawings   *161*

Appendix: *Extracts from various lectures*   *169*

Afterword by David Adams
  From Queen Bee to Social Sculpture:
  The Artistic Alchemy of Joseph Beuys   *187*

Index   *215*

• Introduction

LOOKING BACK at the twentieth century, we can certainly see tremendous progress in all fields of technology. Advancement in this sphere of our human lives, however, has been achieved at the cost of a gradual loss of the instinctual, holistic knowledge that has guided and protected life on Earth for great spans of time. But it would be wrong to nourish a desire for a return to the "good old days." Fortunately, they cannot be retrieved. New ways of tapping this knowledge must be found while retaining the accomplishments of our scientifically trained intelligence.

In order to focus with our sharpened intellect on the physical, material side of nature, we have had to neglect the dimension that constitutes the underlying cause and support of our physical world: the spiritual world. Whether we acknowledge that world or not, the fact that we are confronted with an avalanche of life-negating and life-destroying events cannot be denied, and the underlying causes must be found if we, the Earth, and all its life are to survive. The dying of honeybees in large areas of the world is only one fragment in this whole picture.

What can we do about a situation of such global dimensions? Times of crises, whether personal, nationwide, or global, are times of chance and opportunity. These "moments" in history wake us and shake us up so that we can abandon the path of (self) destruction, change our course, and head in a new direction that offers possibilities for life. Without regaining an all-encompassing knowledge—this time not instinctual or traditional—we can gain no real truth. We are floundering on a sea of hypotheses about the origin of life, about our cosmos, evolution, and the goal of evolution. It takes an honest scientist such as Steven Hawkins to acknowledge that our worldview today is based on assumption: "Any physical theory is always provisional, in the sense that it is only a hypothesis: you can never prove it.... Today scientists describe the universe in terms of two basic partial theories.... The major theme of this book ... is the search for a new theory."[1] The problem, however, is that the general public takes these assumptions as facts—and lives by them.

Rudolf Steiner (1861–1925) did not discard the intellectual accomplishments of our scientific age but, by utilizing them, researched another dimension, which is needed to complement the admirable achievements of the natural, physical and psychological sciences of our time. His method, called "spiritual science," or "anthroposophy" (*anthropos* = humankind, *sophia* = wisdom), can be learned by anyone who applies great stamina of will, concentration, and intent. By reaching into the realms of the reality that causes and affects the sense-perceptible, material world, Steiner was able to cut through the jungle of hypotheses and theories that directly or indirectly influence our everyday actions.

Steiner passed on his research results in approximately forty written works and two thousand lectures. The results of his investigations into spiritual realities are not intended to be "believed"; rather, we are to verify them through common sense and wakeful, open, and unbiased minds. Through

---

1. Stephen Hawking, *A Brief History of Time*, pp. 10–12, (New York: Bantam Books, 1988).

application to everyday, practical life, the fruits of these insights have become abundant throughout the world—in pedagogy, curative education, medicine, agriculture, religion, the arts, the sciences, and in the social realm.

We can be immensely grateful that we also have these lectures on bees from a spiritual scientific view. Steiner gave these lectures to the workers at the Goetheanum in Dornach, Switzerland. Among the workers was a professional bee-keeper, Mr. Müller, who contributed to these lectures in the form of insights and questions. Mr. Müller rebelled vehemently and showed no understanding, however, when Steiner explained the intricacies of the queen bee, mentioning that the modern method of breeding queens (using the larvae of worker bees, a practice that had already been in use for about fifteen years) would have long-term detrimental effects—so grave that "a century later all breeding of bees would cease, if only artificially produced bees were used" (appendix, extract, Nov. 10, p. 177–178). The answer came in another lecture: "It is quite correct that we can't determine this today; it will have to be delayed until a later time. Let's talk to each other again in one hundred years, Mr. Müller, then we'll see what kind of opinion you'll have at that point" (Dec. 5, p. 75).

Seventy-five years have passed, and the kind of queen breeding Steiner spoke of has not only continued, but has become the standard, and is now supplemented with artificial insemination. Now that over 60 percent of the American honeybee populations have died during the past ten years, we should certainly become more alert and open to such statements. Of course, this would force us to take a pause from looking at what appears to be the cause of this crisis— the varroa mite—and pose more difficult questions. These are questions about the general health of the animal and questions that probe basic issues, such as our attitude toward the bee and our depth of understanding for this being. These two factors, which are certainly interrelated, essentially determine the myriad aspects of beekeeping: the form and material of the hive, wax production, artificial foundations, modern queen breeding (including artificial insemination), swarming or its prevention, manipulation of the drone population, sugar feeding, pollen substitutes, moving the hives from location to location, and the yearly exchange of queens. Certainly other "external," physically detrimental factors play a role in beekeeping, but they are also related to our lack of a true understanding of intricate interrelationships and life processes in nature: the effects of mineral fertilizers on the quality of nectar and pollen, insecticides, air and water pollution, and the constantly dwindling variety and quantity of wild flowers.

In order to do justice to an animal—and as human beings this is, or should be, a moral obligation—we must have a deep understanding of its nature. We cannot simply consider our own comfort and calculate our economic situation. If we do, we will face dire consequences.

Rudolf Steiner never intended to turn the clock back to old ways, and as we study these lectures we can glimpse deeply into the nature of the bee. We will then, out of freedom and insight, be able to keep bees in ways that are appropriate to them; we will be able to help them regain life forces and, thereby, heal some of the wounds we have inflicted through shortsightedness, ignorance, and greed. Such study can help us to realize the immensely important role not only of the bee and her honey, but also of the wasp and the ant in nature and human evolution. Can we ignore doing everything possible in attempting to help these creatures? They certainly deserve our active gratitude.

Steiner wanted to look at the situation again with Mr. Müller in a hundred years. Three fourths of that time has passed, and, in all probability, the next few years will be decisive; we will either reverse the trend or see the results Steiner foresaw. Such a development will have an inconceivable impact on the whole ecosystem and on all of nature's intricate interrelationships. The last two of these lectures to the workers should make this clear.

This new translation will help the reader of today understand what Steiner intended to say; in my opinion, it has come just in time, and we are very grateful for it. May these ideas reach the minds and hearts of many!

Gunther Hauk

January 1998

GUNTHER HAUK is director of the Pfeiffer Center, a biodynamic research center sponsored by Threefold Educational Foundation and Sunbridge College, Spring Valley, N.Y. He started a training program in biodynamic gardening there in 1996. He has worked with bees since 1975 and has been a beekeeper since 1980. He gives workshops throughout the United States on the plight of the honey-bee.

• Prelude

Dornach, February 3, 1923

Good morning, gentlemen. Since our last meeting have you thought of any questions you would like to ask me?

(A question was asked about the difference between bees and wasps.)

Dr. Steiner: In asking his question the gentleman in the audience, as an expert bee-master, draws attention to the differences between the life of the bees and that of the wasps. There is much that is similar here, and I have recently described the life of the wasps to you. The life of the bees much resembles it, but, on the other hand, in the beehive there is a very special and remarkable life. How can we account for this?

Life in a beehive is established with extraordinary wisdom behind it. Anyone who has observed life in the beehive will say that. Naturally, you can't say that bees possess a knowledge or science such as human beings do; they simply don't have a brain as we do. They can't take up into their bodies a general understanding of things in this world. However, cosmic influences have a tremendous effect upon the beehive. You would be able to gain a correct and true understanding of life within the beehive if you were to allow for the fact that everything in the environment that surrounds the Earth in all directions has an extremely strong influence on what goes on in the beehive. Life in the beehive, much more so than with ants and wasps, is based on successfully cooperating and working with the other bees in the hive. If you try to figure out how this comes about, you will, after careful observation, draw the following conclusion. The bees have a life in which that element is suppressed, very strongly suppressed, which in other animals is expressed through their sexual life. With bees, this element is very much repressed.

You see, with bees it is always the case that only very few chosen females, the queen bees, take care of all the propagation of the species. With the rest, the sexual life is more or less repressed, but in this sexual life there is another element— love life—which is, above all, a matter concerning the soul. Only when the soul element works on certain organs of the body do these organs become a manifestation, an expression of love life. Since this love life is held back in all the bees except a single queen, the sexual life of the beehive is transformed into all this activity that the bees develop among themselves. That is why those much older and wiser people of a time long ago, "knew" about this in a very different way than the way we know things today; they knew that the wonderful activity of the beehive pointed back to the condition of the bees' love life, the love life that these people associated in their minds with the planet Venus.

About this we can say the following. If you try to describe, on the one hand, wasps and ants in this regard, then they are considered animals that remove themselves more from the influence of the planet Venus. Bees, on the other hand, are completely open to this influence and develop this love life throughout the entire bee colony. This is a very wise form of life, for you can imagine how wise it would have to be. I've told you various things about their method of propagation. There is unconscious wisdom in it, a wisdom that they develop in their observable activities. That which we experience within ourselves only at a time when our hearts develop love is actually the very same thing that is present as a substance in the entire beehive. The whole beehive is permeated with life based on love. In many ways the bees renounce love, and thereby this love develops within the entire beehive. You'll begin to understand the life of bees once you're clear about the fact that the bee lives as if it were in an atmosphere pervaded thoroughly by love.

But the thing that a bee profits from the most is that it derives its sustenance from the very parts of a plant that are pervaded by the plant's love life. The bee sucks its nourishment, which it makes into honey, from the parts of a plant that are steeped in love life. And the bee, if you could express it this way, brings love life from the flowers into the beehive. So you'll come to the conclusion that you need to study the life of bees from the standpoint of the soul.

This is less true with ants and wasps. If you study how they live, you will see that they are not like bees in this respect, that they engage in a more sexual behavior. The bee, with the exception of the queen bee, is a being that would say, if I may put it this way: "As individuals we want to renounce all sexual life, so that we make each one of us into a supporter of the hive's love life." They have indeed carried into the hive that which lives in the flowers. When you begin to think through all of this properly, you will have unlocked the whole secret of the beehive. The living element of this thriving, germinating love that is spread out over the flowers is also contained in the honey the bees make.

You can study this matter further by eating the honey. What does the honey do? ... Honey creates sensual pleasure, at the most, on the tongue. At the moment when you eat honey, it creates the proper connection and relationship between the airy and fluid elements in the human being. There is nothing better for a human being than to add a little honey in the right quantity to food. In a very wonderful way, the bees see to it that a person learns to work on the internal organs by means of this soul element. By means of the honey, the bee colony returns to humans the amount of effort the soul needs to expend in their bodies.... Whenever someone adds honey to food, that person wants to prepare the soul element for properly working upon the body, for breathing, as it were. This is why beekeeping can be a great aid to human culture; it makes human beings strong....

You see, when you consider that bees are influenced most of all by cosmic forces, then you will also see that bees provide the detour for humans to take into their beings what is right and necessary. Everything that is alive will function in the proper manner when it is combined in the correct way. Whoever looks at a beehive should actually say with an exalted frame of mind, "Making this detour by way of the beehive, the entire cosmos can find its way into human beings and help to make them sound in mind and body." ... Thus, you will arrive at the point of expanding wisdom about the nature of humans to include true knowledge of the cosmos.

· Lecture One

Dornach, November 26, 1923

Good morning, gentlemen! I intended to make several comments regarding Mr. Müller's explanations.[1] You might find these comments interesting, although there naturally would not be enough time to really apply such things in apiculture in a practical way at the present time. Since Mr. Müller has presented everything you need to know in such a fine manner, a manner frequently employed today, there is really not much more, if anything at all, to be said about the practical aspects of beekeeping.

Perhaps you noticed something about the entire nature of beekeeping, something, I would say, of the nature of an enigma. The beekeeper is understandably interested above all in what must be done. Actually, every human being should show the greatest interest in this subject, because, much more than you can imagine, our lives depend upon beekeeping. Let's look at this matter from a broader perspective. You see, bees—if you remember Mr. Müller's lectures—are capable of gathering what is already contained in the plants as nectar. In reality they collect only the nectar, and we, as human beings, take only a part, not even a very large part, of what they collect in their hives. You could perhaps state that the amount removed by humans is approximately 20 percent. This is how much we take away from the bees.

---

1. This lecture was given after a report by Mr. Müller, a beekeeper.

Besides this, however, the bee can remove pollen from the plants because of its body shape and the way it is organized as an insect. The bee collects from the plants that very thing which is uncommon and difficult to procure. By means of little brushes located on its hind legs, the bee collects the comparatively small amount of pollen available to it and then either stores or eats it in the beehive. In the specific case of the bee, we have an animal that collects and uses in its household this substance that has been prepared by nature to be in an extraordinarily refined state.

Let's continue. After the bee—and this is perhaps the least apparent feature because people don't think of this at all—has transformed the food in its digestive system into wax (this wax the bee makes by itself), it creates a small vessel to deposit eggs but also to store its provisions. This little container is a great curiosity, I would say. This receptacle looks like this: from above it's hexagonal—from the side like this [see drawing below, also table II in the section of blackboard drawings beginning on page 161]—and on the one side it is closed off like this. Into this receptacle the bee places the eggs and also the provisions. One is right next to another. These things fit together very well, so that in the honeycomb, by means of this plate with which one such cell—this is what it is called—is attached to another, the space in the honeycomb is used to its best possible advantage.

If you ask just why it is that the bee can construct instinctively such an ingeniously shaped cell, people usually respond by saying that they do this to use space efficiently. Yes, that is also true. If you were to imagine any other form of cell, there would always be an empty space between cells somewhere. With this form, no such gap arises, but rather everything is compact so that the space in the honeycomb is completely utilized.

Well, that certainly is one reason. But it is not the only reason. Just consider the following. If the maggot, or larva, is in the cell, then it is completely closed off from the environment. You should not believe for even a moment that whatever exists somewhere in nature is without certain powers. This six-cornered little case, this six-sided shell, has energies within it; it would be quite a different situation if the larva were inside a sphere. The significance of being placed into such a hexagonal house has a very different effect on its contents. The larva internalizes these forms; in its body it senses that in its youth, while its body was as soft as it would ever be, it was in such a six-sided cell. Out of this same energy that it assimilates as a larva, it will, as an adult, produce such a cell out of itself. In it reside the energies that help the bee do all other kinds of work as well. The environment is the cause for everything the bee does externally. This is the first thing we have to pay attention to.

But you have heard from the explanation Mr. Müller gave that there is yet another very remarkable fact. In the entire beehive you find various types of cells. I think a beekeeper can easily tell the female worker bee cells apart from the male drone cells. That isn't very difficult, is it? An even easier task is to distinguish the worker and drone cells from the queen bee cells, because the latter do not have this form; their form is actually more like a pouch. There are also very few of them in a beehive. The worker bees and drones develop in such six-sided cells, but the queens develop in a pouch; hence the latter do not take any notice of what such a many-sided environment means to the other bees.

Add to that something else. To reach full maturity, the queen needs only sixteen days [table II]. At that time it is already a fully grown queen. A worker needs about twenty-one days, a longer period. You could say that nature uses more care in creating the final shape of workers than it does with queens. You'll see shortly that there is another reason for this. Well, so the workers need twenty-one days. The drones, which are used up fastest by the beehive—these male bees are killed when they have fulfilled their purpose—need twenty-three to twenty-four days. You see, this is an entirely new matter. The various bee types (queens, workers, drones) need a different number of days to achieve maturity.

Well, gentlemen, with regard to these twenty-one days a worker needs to develop, there is something rather peculiar. Twenty-one days is not a random number without any particular significance for all the things that happen here on Earth. Twenty-one days is the approximate time span the Sun needs to revolve once on its axis and return to the point where it can begin a new cycle. Just imagine, the worker bee's development is just barely completed at the same time that the Sun has completed a single revolution on its axis. By following this cycle, gentlemen, the worker bee has experienced every different effect the Sun can have on it, and all of these effects are now within the bee.

If this process were to continue beyond twenty-one days, the workers would only receive more of the same and repeat that to which they had already been exposed. If you then imagine the worker here (drawing on the blackboard) [table II, upper left, inner circle] and the Sun over there when the egg is laid, then this is the point that lies opposite the Sun. The Sun turns on its axis once in twenty-one days. Then it will arrive again at this point and begin repeating this movement. The worker uses from the Sun just what it needs to achieve its full development. If the worker were to continue in its development beyond this point, it would leave the Sun development and come into the sphere of influence that the Earth would exert upon its development. It would thus lose its Sun development because it had already completed it and enjoyed it to its fullest capacity. The way it is now, the worker enters into Earth development and experiences it only as an already completely developed animal, having achieved its full maturity at twenty-one days. At most, it needs to experience only, I would say, a moment of Earth development for itself; after this the worker is cut off from further development and is a Sun animal containing the results of all the possible effects that the Sun can have upon such a form of animal life.

Now consider the drone. It doesn't "feel," as I would put it, that it is completed at twenty-one days and wants to continue into the Earth development phase before it is finished maturing. It is definitely an Earth animal, while the worker is a Sun child, complete within itself.

And what about the queen bee? It doesn't even finish the entire Sun cycle of twenty-one days. It lags behind and remains forever a Sun child. The queen lingers to a certain degree in its larval stage, or at least closer to this stage than the other bees. The drones have distanced themselves farthest of all from this larval stage. Because the queen remains closer to the larval stage, it is capable of laying eggs. With bees, you can really see what it means to be under the influence of the Earth or of the Sun: depending upon whether a bee waits to complete the Sun development phase, it will turn out to be a queen, a worker, or a drone. The queen can lay eggs because the Sun effect is always within it, and it hasn't anything at all of the Earth's effect upon development. The worker continues its development for four to five days longer. It makes use of every influence the Sun has to offer. But then it enters slightly, for just a moment, into the Earth development's sphere of influence, just at a point when its body has become hard enough. Because it has absorbed itself completely, it can't return to the Sun development's influence. This is why it can't lay eggs.

The drones are fertile males; this fertilization capability comes from the Earth. The drones acquire the power to fertilize from the few days longer they are exposed, as incomplete insects, to the influence of Earth development. This leads us to the conclusion that with bees you can see clearly that the male's fertilization powers come from the energies given by the Earth, whereas the female capability to develop eggs derives from the Sun's energies. You see, gentlemen, you can comprehend the great significance of the particular length of time that a being needs to develop. During a certain period something occurs that does not happen in a shorter or longer period, but in the shorter or longer period something else happens.

There is one more thing to consider: the queen develops in sixteen days. Here is its point of complete development (drawing on the blackboard) [table II, upper left, outer circle] that it took as it stood opposite the Sun; it remains within the period of Sun development. The workers complete this Sun rotation period, but they remain within the sphere of the Sun's influence and do not enter the Earth development phase. Because they belong to the same Sun development cycle, they feel related to the queen; they feel themselves tied to the queen. The drones, they say, are traitors; they have already split away from the group and have fallen to Earth. They no longer belong with them. They only tolerate them because they need them. And what do they need them for?

It sometimes happens that a queen is not fertilized and nevertheless lays eggs capable of development. The queen does not need to be fertilized in all instances; she will lay eggs anyhow. This is called, in the instance of bees, a virgin brood. The queen has not been fertilized. Some other insects are capable of doing the same. *Parthenogenesis* is the scientific term for it. But from the eggs that are laid in this way, only drones will hatch! If the queen is not fertilized, no more worker bees and queen bees can be produced, only drones. Such a beehive has no practical use. You can see that with a virgin brood, only the opposite sex can arise, never the same sex. That is a very interesting fact, a fact that is very important for maintaining nature's entire household: fertilization is necessary so that the same sex will be reproduced—naturally only in the lower animals, not in the higher ones. That's why it is that out of bee eggs only drones can be created, if no fertilization has taken place.

Fertilization, on the whole, is a very special matter with bees. It is not as though there were a marriage bed somewhere to which they retire during fertilization, but rather the complete opposite takes place. For fertilization they appear in public, in full sunshine. And specifically—this may seem very strange—they go as high as possible. The queen flies as high as possible toward the Sun, to which she belongs. I have described that for you already. The drone, still able to overcome its own Earth-based powers, despite the fact that it has unified itself with these powers, flies highest of all and can fertilize the queen way up there in the air. Then the queen comes back again and lays her eggs. You see, bees don't have a nuptial bed; they have instead a nuptial flight. When they want fertilization to take place, they strive as much as possible to fly in the direction of the Sun. It is also the case that they need good weather for their nuptial flight; during bad weather nothing will happen. All this demonstrates how the queen maintains a relationship with the Sun. After fertilization has taken place, the workers are produced in the corresponding worker cells. At first, as described to you by Mr. Müller, the little maggots (larvae) develop, which, in turn, grow into adult workers in twenty-one days. In these pouch-like cells a queen develops.

In order to gain insight into what follows, I need to tell you something you will naturally at first admit into your thoughts with reservation and doubt, because you would need to spend more time to really study this matter. It just happens to be this way. I need to tie this in with the infertile worker bee we have just discussed. When the worker, having reached maturity, flies out to seek flowers or trees and can assume a secure position on them by means of its claws (drawing on the blackboard) [table III, page 162, lower right], it then can suck up the honey nectar and collect pollen. It carries the pollen on its body where it has deposited it. There is a special accommodation: the so-called brushes on its hind legs, where the pollen is deposited. But the honey nectar it sucks up with its proboscis. Part of this honey serves as food for its own digestion, but the greatest portion it retains in its "honey stomach." The contents of the latter it will regurgitate when it returns to the hive. So when we eat honey, we are in reality eating the regurgitated product of the bee. We need to be clear about this, however; it is a very pure and sweet form of vomit, not the way such products usually are in nature. So, you see, the bee collects what it needs to eat, to store away, or to use in making wax and so on.

Now we need to ask ourselves how the bee finds its way to the blossoms. It makes its way to these blossoms with utter confidence. This is hard to understand, if you look at the bee's eyes. The worker—the drones have somewhat larger eyes—has two little eyes on each side and three very small ones in its forehead (drawing on the blackboard) [table II, upper right]. If you examine the workers' eyes, you will come to the conclusion that they can see very little, and the three tiny eyes, at least at first, seem to be able to see nothing at all. This is what is so strange: The bee does not approach a blossom by means of sight, but by means of something closer to smelling it. It moves in the direction of the scent, which directs it toward the blossom. What leads the bee to the blossom is a certain sensing ability situated midway between smell and taste. The worker bee already "tastes" the nectar and pollen as it flies toward the blossom. Even from a distance it can taste it. That has brought the bee into a situation where it does not use its eyes.

Now just imagine very clearly the following. Think of a queen bee that has just been born, born in the realm of the Sun without having completely absorbed all the influences that the total Sun cycle of twenty-one days could offer it. This queen has been held back somewhat in receiving all of the Sun's influential powers. A whole army of workers has completed the entire Sun cycle of influences but has not gone over and allowed the Earth's influences to take over. Now these workers feel related to the queen not because they have experienced all the same influences of the Sun, but rather because they have remained within the sphere of the Sun's cycle of influences. In this regard, their development was the same as the queen's. The drones do not share this parallel development, since they separated themselves from the rest.

But now the following takes place. Whenever a new queen is created, a nuptial flight must have preceded this birth. The animal, the queen, has come out into the Sun; a new queen bee has been born. At this point a very strange event occurs for all the workers that feel related to the old queen. Their tiny eyes begin to see, at the time when a *new* queen is born. This is something the bees can't stand. They can't bear the fact that something the same as they themselves is arising from somewhere else. The three tiny eyes of the workers originate from deep within their bodies and are permeated with their inner blood, among other things. These eyes have not been exposed to the external effects of the Sun's influence. Because the new queen, having been "born of the Sun," brings new sunlight into the beehive with her own body, the workers with their tiny eyes suddenly begin to "see"; I would like to say, they become clairvoyant and can't stand to see the light emanating from the new queen. The entire horde begins swarming. It is as if they are afraid of the new queen because she seems to blind them. It would be as though you were looking directly at the Sun. This is why they swarm out of the hive. At this point you must try to establish the beehive again with the old queen, attempting to retain most of the workers that still belong to it. The new queen must attract a new community of bees.

A part of the swarm remains behind, but that is the portion that was born under other conditions. The reason bees swarm out of the hive is simply that the workers can't endure the new influence of the Sun that the new queen brings into the hive. Now you might ask, Why do the bees become so overly sensitive to this new Sun effect? Gentlemen, there is a remarkable thing at work here. You know that sometimes meeting up with a bee can turn into an unpleasant experience. It can sting you. Being as large as a human being means that you will usually suffer only an inflammation on your skin—but unpleasant it remains. Little animals can die from the sting. All this derives from the fact that the bee has a stinger that is actually a duct. In this duct something resembling a piston goes up and down, retrieving from the poison sac the poison it causes to stream downward.

This poison, which causes such unpleasant problems for anyone who encounters it, is extraordinarily important for bees. It is not even a pleasant experience for a bee to have to sacrifice the poison while engaged in stinging. The reason it does so is that it has difficulty tolerating all types of external influences. It wants to remain within itself. The bee's world is its own beehive; every influence from the outside disturbs it. It defends itself against this foreign influence with its poison. But this poison has another significance as well. This poison is present within the bee in such a way that only tiny amounts are absorbed into the bee's body. Looking at the worker's eyes, you can say that these tiny eyes can't see. The reason for this is that poison constantly enters these small eyes. This poison is limited in its effect upon the bee when the new queen, the new Sun's influence, is present. The poison loses its effectiveness. Suddenly the eyes can see again. You could say that the bee actually owes to the poison it carries the fact that it lives in a continual twilight.

If I should try to give you a picture of what the bees experience when a new queen crawls out of its sac-like cell, I would have to say that a little bee, like the ones we are examining, lives in a continuous twilight; it feels its way about by means of a sense midway between smell and taste and lives in a twilight that is appropriate for its life as a bee. The appearance of the new queen can be compared to our going out on a dark June night and seeing glowworms, lightning bugs, or fireflies flying about. In the same way, the queen appears to give off light for the swarm of bees, because their poison no longer has an effect strong enough to keep each one "within itself." The bee needs to be shut off from the world with a twilight barrier. This barrier it carries along with itself when it flies out, because the poison can help the bee remain within itself. It needs the poison whenever it becomes afraid that something external might attempt to influence it. The whole beehive wants to be completely by itself. So that the queen can remain in the realm of Sun influences, it may not be in such a cell with corners, but rather in one with round sides. There it will be totally under the Sun's influence [table II, middle right].

And now, gentlemen, we come upon something that should make everyone become interested in apiculture. Inside the beehive things basically happen the same way, only with slight differences, as they do in the head of a human being. The only difference is that the substances do not develop and mature as much. In the human head we have nerves, blood vessels, and also individual protein cells, which remain round. They are always somewhere in there. We have three types of things in the human head. First we have the nerves, consisting of individual cells, which do not grow and develop into animals because they are covered on all sides by nature. They really want to become little animals, these nerves. If the nerve cells in the human head could develop in all directions like the beehive, then these nerve cells would become drones. Second, the blood cells, flowing in the arteries, would become worker bees [see drawing below, also table III, upper left]. Third, the protein cells, particularly those in the middle of the head, having undergone the shortest development, can be compared to the queen bee. So, you see, we have the same three powers in the human head.

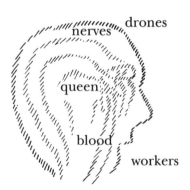

Well, the workers bring home what they collect from the plants, manufacture wax within their own bodies, and then construct these wonderful cells. Gentlemen, this is what the blood cells in the human head do as well! They go from the head into the entire body. If, for example, you look at a piece of bone, you will see everywhere these hexagonal cells. The blood that circulates in the body carries out the same task that the bees do in the beehive. The only difference is that other cells, for example, the muscles—where it is also still similar, for muscle cells are also similar to the wax cells of the bees—soon lose their form as they are dissolved. They are still soft, so you don't notice it as much. But if you study the matter more closely, you will notice this form in the bones very clearly. So now we can say that our blood has the same powers that a worker bee has.

Yes, gentlemen, you can study this even in connection with time. Those cells that you find developed before everything else in the human embryo, and which then remain—the protein cells—are the very cells that are present in the earliest stages of embryonic development. The others, the blood cells, develop somewhat later, and last of all the nerve cells appear. It happens the same way in the beehive, the only difference being that a human being builds up a body that only seems to belong to the individual, and the bee also constructs a body: the honeycomb, the cells. The same things happen with the construction of wax that happen in the forming of our bodies. With the body it is not easy to prove that the blood cells make it out of a type of wax. But we are made of a kind of wax, just as the bees make their honeycomb in there or in the box. So we can say that it is like this: the human being has a head, and the head works on the entire large body, which actually is the beehive. And the beehive contains within it in the relationship between the queen and the workers, the same relationship that the protein cells that remain round have with the blood. And the nerves are constantly being ruined. Continually the nerves are being worn out, for we exhaust our entire nervous system. When this happens, we do not immediately engage in a battle of nerves—we would die each year if we did that—the way the bees engage in a battle against the drones; nevertheless, our nerves become weaker each year. It is actually because of this weakening of the nerves that the human being dies. We are then no longer able to sense the body as well as we once did, and human beings always die because they have frayed their nerves and worn them out.

If you now examine the human head, which represents the beehive, you will find that everything in the head is protected. If you bring something forcibly up to it from the outside, there will be a terrible injury. The head can't tolerate it. The beehive also can't tolerate the appearance of a new queen and would rather leave than try to live with this new queen. It is for this reason that apiculture has always been considered extremely important to human beings. Humans take 20 percent of the honey away from the bees. You could easily say that this honey is extraordinarily useful to us, because we would otherwise obtain very little honey in all the other food we eat, since it is so sparingly distributed among plants. We would otherwise manage to eat only tiny amounts of honey. We also have "bees" in us—specifically, our blood, which carries this honey to the various parts of the human body. This very same honey is what the bee needs to make wax, from which it can construct its body: the honeycomb of the beehive.

Honey has an extraordinarily beneficial effect on humans, particularly when we grow old—with a child, it is milk that acts in this way. Honey assists in maintaining the form of our bodies. For this reason the consumption of honey is highly recommended for older people. However, it is important not to eat too much of it. If you overeat honey and don't use it to simply garnish other foods, then you will develop too much form. Then the body form will become brittle, and you will contract many diseases. Well, a healthy person senses how much should be eaten. Particularly for older people, honey is an extraordinarily healthy form of nourishment, because it actually gives the body a solidness, a real power of resistance.

If you were, therefore, to follow this rule also with children who have rickets—to be sure, you would not do this during the very first weeks of life, when children normally would live only on milk, because honey would not have any effect then—if you gave a such a child at about nine to ten months of age a properly dosed amount of honey and then had the child continue this diet until age three or four, the rickets would not become as bad as it would normally be, because the nature of rickets is that it keeps the body too soft, so that it begins to collapse into itself. But honey contains the power to maintain the shape and form of the human body, to give it solidity. You need to gain insight into the interconnections of these matters. You really could say that we ought to pay much more attention to honey production and beekeeping than we currently do.

The following is also possible. In nature there are remarkable connections between all things. Those particular laws that people can't comprehend with their ordinary understanding are actually the most important. It is true, isn't it, that these laws operate in such a way as to always allow for a slight amount of freedom or latitude. Take, for instance, the balance between the sexes on Earth. There is not a completely equal number of men and women on Earth, but the number is approximately equal. Over the entire Earth the number is just about equal. The wisdom of nature controls this. If the time should ever come—I think I told you this before—that we are able directly to manipulate the birth of children by sex and leave the choice to the parents, then the whole matter could immediately become chaotic. Currently the situation is this: If, for example, raging wars have decimated the population in some region, then the population becomes more fruitful, and more children are born. In nature every deficiency, every shortage, calls forth an opposing power.

It is also true that when bees seek out honey nectar in a certain region, they remove it from the plants. But they take it away from the plants that we need for other purposes, such as for fruits and so forth. The strange thing is that fruit trees and similar plants thrive better in regions where there is apiculture than in regions where there is not. When the bees remove the honey nectar from the plants, nature does not look idly by, but creates even more such fruitful plants. So it is that the human being derives benefits not only from the honey the bees provide but also from that which is offered by the plants that bees have visited. This is an important law, into which you can gain deep insight.

Connected to all of this is the thought that if you could see to the bottom of things, you could express the following. Nature has placed a truly wonderful wisdom into the entire manner in which a bee society functions. Bees respond to certain powers of nature that are extremely important and really wonderful. That is why you will feel a certain reserve that will keep you from indiscriminately, and perhaps crudely, trying to put your fingers on these powers of nature. It is still true today that wherever we intrude upon these powers of nature, we tend to make things worse rather than better. But we don't worsen things immediately, since nature has limitations everywhere. Despite these constraints, nature operates in the best way it can. We can remove certain limitations and thereby make things a little easier for nature. We have, for instance, seemingly really helped nature very much in regard to beekeeping by using, instead of the older beehives, the newer type of beehive boxes that are arranged with comfort in mind for both bee and human.

But now we come to this whole new chapter concerning the artificial breeding of bees. Gentlemen, you must not believe that I can't understand, even from the standpoint of non-anthroposophic science, that, beginning with the very first steps, much can be said for artificially breeding bees, because it does simplify quite a few things. But the strong bonding of a bee generation, a bee family, will be detrimentally affected over the longer period. In certain respects you will be able to only praise artificial breeding, if all necessary precautions are taken, as Mr. Müller described to us. But we'll have to wait and see how things will look after fifty to eighty years. Certain forces that have operated organically in the beehive until now will become mechanized, will in themselves be mechanically carried out. It won't be possible to establish the intimate relationship between a queen bee you have purchased and the worker bees the way it would arise all by itself in nature. But at the beginning, the effects of this are not apparent.

Obviously I would not like to see initiated a fanatic movement against the artificial breeding of bees. Such things should not be undertaken when we know that other, more practical means exist. Being fanatic about this would be about the same as something else I want to tell you about. We could figure out approximately when the Earth's reserves of coal will be exhausted. Then we could decide to extract a smaller amount of coal, so that the reserves would last until the Earth reaches the projected end of its existence. You can't say that you must do this, because you really ought to be optimistic and put some trust in the future. You must then tell yourself, well, all right, we'll rob the Earth of all its coal, which means, in reality, that we'll rob our descendants of coal. But they will be able to find another source of energy, so that they won't need coal. In the same way, you could, of course, talk about the disadvantages in the artificial breeding of bees.

But, nevertheless, it doesn't hurt to be conscious of the fact that by introducing a mechanical, artificial element, we are actually disturbing what nature has produced in such a wonderful manner. Beekeeping has always been considered an activity full of wonder; particularly in earliest antiquity, the bee was regarded as a sacred animal. Why? From the manner in which this revered animal carries out its tasks, you could begin to understand much about how things happen within the human being's body. If you take a piece of beeswax into your hands, you are actually looking at an intermediary product arising from a mixture of blood, muscles, and bones, more precisely that which lies between the latter three. Humans undergo such a stage of wax production; the wax does not solidify, but rather remains fluid until it can be transformed into blood, muscle, or bone cells. The beeswax that you can see physically is within you in the form of certain powers and energies.

When, in olden times, people made candles from beeswax and lit them, they really saw in them a remarkable sacrament: "This wax, burning there before us, we obtained from the beehive. There it was a solid substance. When the fire melts this wax and it evaporates, then the wax takes on the same condition that it has in our own bodies."

Back then people sensed in the burning candle wax something in their own bodies that flies toward heaven in a similar fashion. This put them into a special mood of reverence that caused them to regard the bee as a particularly sacred animal, because it prepared something that the human being must continually prepare within. For this reason, it is also true that the more we go back in time, the more we will find that people revered the existence and conduct of bees. Of course, this was when bees were still in a wild state in nature. People looked upon them as a revelation. Later they were domesticated. But in all the things that occur among the bees, there are truly marvelous riddles. The only way to understand bees is to direct the efforts of your study toward what it is that actually happens between the human head and the rest of the body.

Now I have finished making these comments. Wednesday we will have our next session. Perhaps you will think of some questions to bring up at that time. Mr. Müller may also think of one thing or another to ask. I wanted to make only these comments, which are not open to doubt because they are based on true knowledge gained by expending great effort in obtaining these insights. But there still may remain a question of perhaps trying to clarify this matter or that.

• Lecture Two

Dornach, November 28, 1923

Good morning, gentlemen! Has any question come to mind that you would still like to ask me?

At this point, someone reads aloud an article printed in the Swiss Apiculture Newspaper, *new series, nos. 2 and 3, February and March 1923. The article by Professor Buttel-Reepen is entitled "Can Bees See Colors Invisible to Human Beings?"*

Dr. Steiner: Let's talk about this a bit. These experiments carried out by Forel, as well as Kühn and Pohl, demonstrate clearly how thoughtlessly such experiments are conducted at the present time.[1] You cannot imagine anything more absurd than the manner in which this experiment is interpreted! Simply consider for a moment that I could also interpret it in the following way. Assume, for instance, I have a substance (such substances do exist) that is particularly sensitive to ultraviolet light, by that I mean those colors in the color spectrum that lie beyond the visible blue and violet colors. Take, as a specific example, the substance mentioned in the article: the acid salt *hexacyanoplatinate*. The latter will give off light

---

1. Auguste Henri Forel, 1848-1931, a Swiss psychiatrist and natural scientist who wrote, among other things, *The Psychic Capabilities of Ants*, 1901, and *How Insects Live Through Their Senses*, 1910; Alfred Kühn, 1885-1968, a German zoologist who wrote and compiled *An Outline of General Zoology*, 1922; no information on Pohl.

even if I have darkened all the colors of the visible spectrum [page 163, table IV, upper left]. For this purpose I create a device that will eliminate red, orange, yellow, green, blue, indigo, and violet so that they will not be visible. As a result, I will have here the so-called ultraviolet rays, which are invisible to the human eye. If I put this chemical compound, hexacyanoplatinate, a white powder, where it will be exposed to these rays in a darkened room, then it will begin to phosphoresce. As human beings, we can see nothing in this completely darkened room, but now we allow light rays to enter. At this point we apply the device to remove the visible spectrum, thereby allowing only ultraviolet rays to enter. But when I place the hexacyanoplatinate where the rays should fall, what happens? Then this substance "sees."

The whole procedure would be about the same if you were to use ants for an experiment instead. Rather than taking hexacyanoplatinate, I take ants. Ants are attracted to sugar. As a result, I say to myself that they can "see." But they do not have to see the sugar to find it, just as little as the hexacyanoplatinate needs to be able to see in order to begin glowing and giving off light. All I can assert now is only that when I have a certain substance, it has an effect on ants. More than that I am not permitted to maintain and say is true. The learned scientists who wrote the article are extremely careless in their thinking and are asserting such things as can be considered only pure fantasy. The only possible assertion that can be maintained is that something did affect these insects through their sense organs to a greater or lesser degree. The scientists in the article proved that no more stimulation of the insects took place when they lacquered their eyes shut. But it was typical for them to apply by analogy to ants and wasps what they had noticed in working with bees. This demonstrates how carelessly such experiments are carried out.

To this we can still add the following point. If you continue going in this direction [see drawing below, also table IV, upper left], you will come to the so-called ultraviolet rays. Here we have red, orange, yellow, green, blue, and then, still further, indigo and violet.

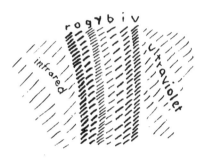

There (pointing to the left side) we have the infrared rays and there (pointing to the right side) the ultraviolet rays. These ultraviolet rays possess the peculiar property, as stated in the article, of having a very strong chemical effect. Whatever you place in the vicinity of these ultraviolet rays will be very strongly affected through a chemical process. As a result of this, if I expose an ant to these rays, it is immediately affected by them. The ant senses them. That statement is true; the ant senses them primarily through its eyes. For the ant, being exposed to the ultraviolet rays creates a feeling as if someone were tickling it. It is the same with the hexacyano-platinate that is affected when it is placed in the realm of chemical activity. If I draw the shades in a room and allow only the ultraviolet rays to enter, the fact is that the ant notices immediately that something is happening here. Specifically, if you had ant eggs with larvae there in that room, they would undergo a complete change: they would die wherever such a strong chemical effect was being produced. That is why ants in an otherwise dark room will move their eggs away from the ultraviolet rays in order to save them. Well, what it really boils down to in this article is a chemical reaction. That which I mentioned recently in another lecture is certainly correct: bees have a kind of sense organ that combines the characteristics of smell and taste and lies somewhere in the middle between the two. This is what the bees sense (with the ants it is similar).

These gentlemen are so unaware of what really is involved that they do not even know that, for example, when human beings sense colors in their eyes, beginning with the visible violet rays, small chemical reactions take place. Here you can see that the perception of colors in human beings tends to go in the direction of chemical processes. You can say that everything that was examined with regard to the bees can be reduced to the process of bringing about an inner chemical reaction in the bees when they live in an environment that exposes them to ultraviolet light.

Now consider the fact that bees can perceive everything in the area of black, white, yellow, gray (simply a dark white), and blue-green [table IV, upper middle]. There is, after all, no ultraviolet in all these colors. Because of this, they do not sense the strong chemical reaction that takes place when they come into the presence of ultraviolet light. When a bee leaves an area of black, white, yellow, and blue-green and moves into an ultraviolet area, it senses something strange about which it can do nothing. The main consideration here is that the bee has a combination sense of smell and taste. It is true that we make a clear distinction between smelling and tasting. Tasting, for us, is primarily a chemical sense; it is based completely upon chemical processes. But the bee has a sense that lies midway between smelling and tasting.

There is no objection perceived in the fact that a bee can distinguish colors, as exhibited when its hive is painted a specific color that it recognizes. Consider that each color creates a different chemical reaction and has a different degree of warmth [table IV, lower left]. If you were to color a surface red and a bee were to approach it, the bee would feel the warmth of the color. How then is it not possible for this bee to have a different feeling when it comes upon a blue color [table IV, lower middle]. On a blue surface it is colder. The bee senses the warmth of the red and the coldness of the blue. This much it can distinguish. But from this you may not logically deduce that this bee sees with its eyes in the same way human beings do. That would be complete nonsense.

That is the way it is with many other things that people do. I have already pointed out to you in which direction all these experiments are going. I have told you that there is a certain plant—the "Venus flytrap"—that immediately closes its leaves when they are touched. The same way you make a fist when someone wants to touch or hit you, so also does the Venus flytrap wait for an insect to come near it, and then snaps its leaves together. Now people say that this plant, the Venus flytrap, has a soul just like humans. It perceives when the insect arrives, snaps its leaves together, and so on. Then I always answer, I know of a self-acting mechanism that is constructed in such a way that if an animal approaches it and touches some part of it, this mechanism closes immediately, and the animal is caught. This is what you call a mousetrap. If you ascribe a soul to the Venus flytrap, then logically you must say the same thing about the mousetrap. If you credit bees with the sense of sight simply because you observe them acting in a certain way in ultraviolet light, then you must likewise ascribe the same sense of sight to the chemical compound hexacyanoplatinate, which can also, so to speak, see.

If people truly would think, then they would come upon some very remarkable observations, because hexacyanoplatinate is an extraordinarily interesting compound, consisting, among other things, of barium. This is a white metal

belonging to the category of alkaline earth. It is also interesting that such metals play a certain role in human life. We
would not, as human beings, be able to have in our physical
bodies the proper effect of the proteins, as contained in the
egg whites we eat, if it were not for the presence of such
metals in our pancreas. These metals must be there. In barium, we have something that is related to the pleasant feelings we experience in the process of digestion. Platinum, as
you know, is a particularly valuable metal, a precious metal
that is especially hard and heavy. These metals all possess
the characteristic that they, in turn, are connected to that
which is called feeling or sensing.

Let me remind you of something else. In this compound
there is also cyanide. That is a certain kind of hydrocyanic
acid salt, which is also called prussic acid. Now I have told
you before[2] that a human being always develops a certain
kind of prussic acid right where the muscles are used. So we
can say that this entire compound is rather similar to those
substances that a human being continuously creates in the
body. From this you can see that even a human being is
extremely sensitive to the chemical processes that take place
in ultraviolet light, specifically in the chemical components
of light. This sensitivity is registered in the entire body, not
in the eyes. Thus it is possible for us to judge this matter
properly only if we pay close attention to these matters.

Only with the help of anthroposophic science will we be
led to observe such things as the fact that when hexacyanoplatinate is particularly affected by light, one type of feeling is
taking place there. The intensity of this type of activity is
present to the greatest degree in bees. Bees sense the colors

---

2. See lecture "Über Blausäure und Stickstoff, Kohlensäure und Sauerstoff,"
October 10, 1923, in *Mensch und Welt Das Wirken des Geistes in der Natur / Über
die Bienen*, (GA 351; not published in English).

with particular intensity and see dimly luminous colors when other beings emitting light appear in the vicinity. That is why I continue to say that, in general, a bee experiences only dim conditions around itself. If, however, a new queen bee appears on the scene, then the other bees experience the queen bee as a phosphorescent source, very much as we can experience glowworms on a June night. That experience is reserved for the three little eyes of the bee; the other, larger eyes do have some kind of normal light sensitivity, but it resembles a twilight condition. If this normal light is screened out, the animal then perceives more powerfully the presence of a color that brings about a chemical reaction, for example, ultraviolet, or one that creates no chemical reaction, infrared.

At the end of the article referred to earlier, the authors promise future reports on their research with infrared light. To be sure, if bees are exposed to infrared light, they will act quite differently, since the chemical reactions no longer will occur. The facts reported in these experiments are correct, but you need to be quite clear in your minds that the conclusions arrived at by Forel and Kühn are not correct. This is a very thoughtless way to carry out an experiment. But then people say that the findings have been proved beyond any doubt. Yes, they are, naturally—for a person who can ascribe a soul to a mousetrap. But for someone who knows just how far one can go, just how far thoughts may take one so that the experiment can be carried out properly, the authors of the article have not eliminated all reasonable objections to the proofs they have offered.

In everyday affairs we are not used to pursuing a matter at hand with such rigor. When people experience somewhere in their lives an insignificant matter, they can, as the saying goes, make a mountain out of a molehill. This also happens to our learned scientists. When they consider one aspect of an experiment, they do not stop thinking. Instead, they continue thinking about only that which lies directly before their eyes. From this can arise all sorts of fantastic nonsense: a molehill can become a mountain very easily. When modern science claims something to be true, it can do so only through its power—it controls all the scientific journals. As a result, no one generally will dare to contradict whatever has been presented. However, ultimately you will not be able do anything with all this nonsense.

I personally believe that if you were to consult all existing beekeepers, you would find out that the best of them would concern themselves very little with the results that Forel and Kühn published regarding their experiments with bees. This is so because beekeepers need to be practical above all. They do instinctively whatever they need to do. It would be much better if you really understood why these instinctive things are done. I think that I have generally noticed that a beekeeper might be interested enough to sit down and read such an article on a Sunday evening when it is snowing outside. But he will not be able to apply the information in any meaningful way.

But you must certainly have some other interesting questions to ask me.

Mr. Müller: I would like to add something about the queen bee. We've already talked about the fact that it lays eggs. But we also have unfertilized queen bees, for example, in bad weather, and from their eggs the worthless drones hatch. Likewise, the situation arises that when the queen has left and no young brood is present any longer, the worker bees breed a bee to become a queen. This queen also lays eggs, but, as it turns out, unfertilized eggs, from which arise worthless drones.

Then I also would like to make a comment about swarming. The first swarm has no new queen bee; it is still sleeping in its cell. Only the older bees have left with their queen. By catching this queen, I can put all the bees of the swarm in the hive.

In regard to the bee's ability to see, I would like to say that when we work in the bee house and there is too much light—which is never enough light for the beekeeper—the bees get overly excited. About the bees' stinging when they are swarming, all our beekeepers know that a first swarm is rather "ticklish," but the subsequent swarm is less so. Our opinion is that young bees don't sting, still don't use their stinger.

There are some regions where people don't harvest honey before the priest has blessed the hives. August 8 is such a sacred honey day.

It can also happen that a swarm flies out, that the queen takes up a position somewhere else. It then appears that the swarm is done for, but it isn't so; it isn't always completely the case.

Dr. Steiner: Regarding what I said, it all seemed to be directed toward the fact that the old queen leaves its own community of bees when the young queen appears, specifically, when it shows itself to the bees as a "glowworm." When the swarm has swarmed out and you've caught the old queen, then you can bring the swarm back to the hive and it will just continue functioning as it did before. You can't say that it is not true that the swarm, on first impulse, left on account of the strong impression of light the young queen made upon the three small eyes of each bee. You haven't eliminated that possibility entirely. You need to think very logically here. Let me give you an example from real life. Imagine that all of you were working somewhere for the same company. One day you decide to strike because the board of directors did something unjust. Let's assume you decide to strike, which is like swarming out.

Now time passes, and you are no longer able to buy the groceries you need. You're suffering from hunger and are forced to return to work again. Well, can I now say that it isn't true that something unjust happened earlier? For now you must consider that if you remove the old queen from the swarm that left the hive and put the swarm back into the hive, then the swarm will swallow the bitter pill that it no longer has its old queen and will simply have to put up with the new queen—something it does sense. That's why what I said before isn't incorrect; rather it's a question of putting all these things in the proper perspective.

Then you also spoke about premature swarming, where a young queen isn't there yet, where you really can't talk about something like that. Well, have you ever seen such a premature swarming if the egg of the young queen hasn't hatched?

Mr. Müller: Nine days before the young queen hatched.

Dr. Steiner: At first the young queen is in its cell in the form of an egg [table IV, upper right]. After sixteen days she'll be an adult queen bee. At that point she'll emerge from the egg. But nine days earlier she is either in the form of an embryo or a larva. The strange thing is that the egg at that point gives off the greatest amount of light. It gradually stops shining, and the young queen still shines for some time. Her strongest radiation appears when she is still an embryo or a larva. So it becomes quite clear why these premature swarms, consisting of the most sensitive bees, leave the hive. And that explains why nothing happens until a young queen appears. What is the young queen? She is already there, even if only in the form of an embryo.

If the queen remains unfertilized, then she will not produce any workers, only drones, and, as Mr. Müller said, on top of everything, they are bad drones. That's correct. You can't use the brood of an unfertilized, pseudo mother, because there are no workers in it. You'll have to see to it that the bees carry out their nuptial flight specifically under the influence of sunlight.

Now you see again what an important role the chemical element plays, for it's true, isn't it, that everything that happens is an effect exerted upon the sexual nature of bees. The nature of sex is, however, completely of a chemical kind. When the queen flies up high, naturally, light doesn't cause the influence directly, but rather it is the result of the chemical element present in the influence coming from the light. Here you can really see how supersensitive bees are to that which is chemical in nature.

You also stated that if you are working with the hive, you, as a human being, need light, but the bees become restless and would prefer to work in the dark. Well, think about this very hard: The bee receives chemical effects from the light; it is affected chemically by the light. But it is the chemical effects that it senses, not the light as such. Now you come as a human being and allow light to shine on the bees. You suddenly introduce light, which affects bees, just as a strong draft would affect you if you were sitting somewhere and opened a window to allow a strong draft to enter. The bee senses the light; it doesn't sense that it is particularly bright, but it senses it more like a shock that causes it to be shaken up to the point of confusion. You could almost say—without my ever having observed this personally—that when the beekeeper allows too much light to fall into the hive, the bees will act extremely nervous because of the chemical effects of the light within their bodies, and they will begin to fly back and forth like small swallows. They dance back and forth. That's simply an indication that they feel in themselves a certain amount of restlessness. Imagine, for a moment, that the bees did not act restless in this way when they saw the light. They would tend to crawl away into corners so that the light would no longer affect them.

In all these matters you should be clear about the fact that these effects, which are present everywhere, should not be compared to the effects that these same things have upon human beings. In this case, you would anthropomorphize everything too much, and you would never get to the point of being able to imagine the whole matter in any other way than by saying that because the human being sees things this way, the animal, too, must see them the same way. You should not be allowed to say anything like that offhandedly. You probably have already experienced the following situation. Whoever has observed such things can perceive correctly what is going on. In your mind put yourself into a kitchen where there is an oven range plate that is slightly warm because of the pilot light directly beneath it. The cat likes to take up a position there, curls up, closes its eyes, and goes to sleep. Now if, somewhere under a kitchen cabinet, there is a mouse that the cat can't see with its eyes, it can happen that the cat will jump down suddenly without having opened its eyes and, with complete self-confidence, will leap right on top of the mouse. Before you've even had a chance to consider what is happening, the cat comes back with the mouse in its mouth.

Well, gentlemen, you're not going to tell me that the cat saw the mouse; it had its eyes closed and was sleeping. Then other people will say, "The cat has a very fine sense of hearing, and with this it was able to sense where the mouse was." Now you would have to reason as follows. The cat hears best of all when it sleeps. That is a rather questionable assertion, because seeing and hearing are those senses that generally play an important role only while the cat is awake, whereas the sense of smell plays an extraordinarily important role when the cat is asleep. This sense is based upon reacting to chemical processes. Something chemical happens in the nose and in the entire brain. And, moreover, if you hear something, are you immediately prepared to jump with confidence in the right direction? That is certainly not the case. Hearing is not a sense you can orient yourself to so quickly. So it can't be a question of hearing in the case of the cat.

But what you do definitely find in the cat is a very fine sense of smell, which it has right in its bristly whiskers . And this extremely fine sense of smell is in the whiskers because each bristle contains a canal in which is contained a substance (drawing on the blackboard) that changes chemically when a mouse is present. If there isn't a mouse present, then this substance is in a certain chemical state. But if one is in the vicinity, even rather far away, then the cat will sense it through the chemical changes in its whiskers. I once told you[3] about people who live on the fourth floor of a house, in the cellar of which some material, for example, buckwheat, is stored. These people can sense this material and become ill from it. People can easily come to the conclusion that the sense of smell can also function with great accuracy; otherwise there wouldn't be any police dogs. They actually do not achieve very much with their eyes but can accomplish much with their sense of smell. So it turns out that in the animal kingdom, confidence in sense perception does not come from the eyes, but can instead be ascribed to chemical effects, and these effects are strongest of all in ultraviolet light.

If you really wanted to help a police dog, it would be very beneficial to the dog for you to go along with it, shine on it a special spotlight that removes the visible color spectrum, and

3. See lecture "Zur symptomatischen Betrachtung des Astralleibes," April 14, 1923, in *Vom Leben des Menschen und der Erde* (GA 349; not published in English).

make sure that the dog is always within the beam of ultraviolet light. Then the police dog would pursue its quarry with even more confidence, because even greater chemical effects would occur in its scenting hairs—yes, dogs also have "whiskers" for this purpose. Everything that you can know about animals points toward the fact that when you enter the animal kingdom, you need to look beyond such obvious and commonly referred to animal sense organs as sight and hearing, and you must delve into the senses of smell and taste; that means going down to the level of the chemical senses.

You were also of the opinion that young bees don't sting. It could easily be explained that young bees simply haven't yet developed the mature organ for stinging as well as all other inner organs. That will all come later, when it reaches maturity. There is nothing of particular importance about this, and it doesn't contradict what I've already said.

Mr. Müller asks about feeding bees artificially. He takes four liters of water and five kilos of sugar, adds some thyme, chamomile tea, and a pinch of salt. What effects will that have?

Dr. Steiner: We should be able to give quite a bit of information about that because our homeopathic medicines are partially based upon such principles, according to which you acted instinctively. Not all, but a number of our medications are based on them. If you feed bees sugar, it is actually, at first glance, a bit of nonsense. By nature bees derive their nourishment from nectar and pollen, not from sugar.

Mr. Müller: For example, we have to empty out everything in the apiary, even the combs with unhatched bees, because the bees will otherwise get dysentery. And then sometimes the bees have only two to three kilos left at the end of the summer. That's not enough.

Dr. Steiner: Generally bees are not accustomed to eating sugar, since they normally have their honey as food. That's what they're used to taking in by nature. Now the strange thing is that in winter the bee will transform every type of food it receives into a kind of honey. Any animal will transform the nourishment it receives into something it can use. The bee does this as well, but you can imagine that transforming sugar into honey demands more energy from the bee than does eating its own honey. What kind of bees are those going to be that are capable of transforming larger quantities of sugar into honey? Those can only be the strong bees, the ones that you can well use. You won't be able to get weak bees to accomplish this transformation, and for that reason they are more or less useless to humans.

But remember what I said earlier. This whole procedure is understandable from an anthroposophic standpoint. If you add chamomile tea, for example, to the mixture, then you are already taking from the bee a part of the work it would normally have to carry out in its own body. If you mix sugar with this chamomile tea, the chemical substance of chamomile is that part of the plant that brings out the honey nectar within the plant. For the substance contained in chamomile tea is not only in the chamomile plant but also in every plant that has honey nectar in it. The chamomile plant, however, contains this substance to a greater degree, and that's why you can't use it as a plant source for honey. But if you have before you a plant, there is in it a lot of so-called starch. This starch continually has the tendency of transforming itself into sugar. Now the juice of the chamomile plant already begins working on this starch in the plant in such a way that it directs the sugary juice within the plant to become more like honey. If you give the animal chamomile tea, you are supporting it this way in the inner honey effect that it creates. You are making the sugar more like honey when you add chamomile tea.

This is how we also do it with our homeopathic medicines. If you have any kind of metal that you need to give as medicine, you can't give it to a person directly, because it would simply wander through the digestive system without being properly absorbed. What you need to do is compound it with something else, because then it will be more easily assimilated. That's the way it also is with the chamomile tea that you add to the sugar. Salt will also have to be added, because it is salt that makes digestible otherwise indigestible things. Human beings instinctively add salt to soup, because salt has the unique property of spreading very fast within the body, which helps make food digestible.

• Lecture Three

Dornach, December 1, 1923

Gentlemen! Mr. Müller gave me another issue of the *Swiss Apiculture Newspaper,* in which there is an article about the experience people have had with honey cures: "Our continuing experiences with honey cures at the Frauenfelder Home for Children in Amden," by Dr. Paula Emrich, Weesen, no. 3, March 1923.

Several passages are read aloud.

It will be of interest to you to have me add a few comments to this article today. What happened here is that an attempt was made, at this home for children, to treat with honey those children who were found to be undernourished. According to the article, the children received honey dissolved in moderately warm milk, milk that had not been overheated or brought to a boil but had remained below the boiling point.

Dr. Emrich has recorded excellent results to prove her success, namely, that the number of red blood cells in these children increased in a very extraordinary way. She had, for example, two children who were siblings. The younger child, upon entering the home, had only 53 percent red corpuscles. Upon this child's release, after the honey cure had been completed, the red corpuscle count had risen to 82 percent. The older child had a count of 70 percent to begin with and 78 percent when this child was picked up by the parents. The latter child had experienced less of an increase, but at least there was an increase. This child had been given only the milk cure, but the red blood cells had nevertheless risen from 70 to 78 percent; this child had not been so weak to start with, but also did not grow in strength as much as the first child did.

She also lists quite a number of very interesting experiments, and I ask you kindly, when I mention these experiments, to pay attention to the ages of these children. If you want to research the effect that any particular substance might have on human beings, it does no good simply to do these experiments in a laboratory, but rather it is necessary to determine, first of all and immediately, the age of each sick individual before you conduct any experiments with nutrition or make any attempts to effect a cure [table V, a column of numbers, page 163].

We have here the case of an eleven-year-old boy; he underwent a honey cure of eight weeks and, as a result, achieved a very significant improvement in the condition of his glands. His bronchitis diminished, and the red corpuscles, the important constituents of blood, rose in number from 73 to 75 percent [upper right]. A second example is another eleven-year-old boy who experienced an increase from 55 to 74 percent. Then there is a fourteen-year-old girl whose count improved from 70 to 88 percent. I won't read to you all the rest of the numbers, but they are in every instance significant. Dr. Emrich also lists the gains in body weight; they, too, give evidence that the children have become stronger. She also lists three girls, one aged 7 and two aged 10, and six boys aged 7, 8, 9, 11, 12, and 13, respectively. These experiments demonstrate that children in this range of ages, specifically of school age, seem to derive the best benefit from this honey cure.

In addition to these results, the author of this article tried to determine why it is that these children benefited so much from this honey cure. What she states is remarkably interesting. She indicates something that condemns, in the most extreme way, that which is still applied in many areas by contemporary science. What do the foremost scientists do when they want to assess the nutritive value of certain foods? They do a chemical analysis of these foods in order to determine the type and quantity of chemical substances they contain. That's what today's scientists do.

This is what happened. A student, Dr. Emrich says, of the famous professor of physiology, Bunge, whom you all know by name at least, was in Basel and conducted experiments that involved feeding mice milk.[1] These mice had a good life; their physical condition improved tremendously because they were being fed milk. Then he introduced another element into this experiment. He told himself that milk consists of casein, which is the basis of cheese, fat, sugar, and various salts. He said to himself that mice thrive when they are given milk, and milk consists of casein, fat, sugar, and salts [table V]; hence he decided to give a similar group of mice these constituents of milk, which are the same as those found in milk. But the mice to whom he gave casein, fat, sugar, and salts died only a few days later! This group of mice had received exactly the same substances, scientifically analyzed, as the first group, but they died. You see, it doesn't make any difference if you know all the parts of a compound. Something else

---

1. Gustav von Bunge, 1844-1920, a German physiologist of Russian origin. He was a professor in Basel after 1885 and supported the modern notion of *neovitalism*, a renewal of the theory or doctrine that life processes arise from or contain a nonmaterial, vital principle and cannot be explained entirely as physical and chemical phenomena. His main works are *A Handbook of Physiological and Pathological Chemistry*, 1887, and *A Handbook of Human Physiology*, 1901, 2 vols.

must be involved here—that's what these gentlemen should have told themselves.

But what is it that they did tell themselves? The gentlemen said that the substances that can be analyzed chemically are all that there can be; these substances are present everywhere. Wherever something happens, a substance must be involved. But those substances contained in milk (casein, fat, sugar, and salts) are not responsible for the results in this experiment! Then the gentlemen said that there simply must be another new substance in such immeasurably small quantities that chemical analysis does not uncover it. This substance people now call a vitamin. *Vita* is the Latin word for "life"; hence vitamin means "makes life" [table V]. Heine[2] once had in mind to ridicule something. He said that there are people who, for example, would like to explain where poverty comes from, what the cause of poverty is. Well, the simplest explanation is that poverty comes from pauperism [*pauvreté*, the French origin of the English word; *pauper*, the Latin origin]. There you have different words, but they don't really explain anything at all.

I was once in literary society where the discussion turned to the subject of where the comical element came from. A number of people present had given this serious thought and came up with some thought-provoking arguments. But then one of them stood up and walked to the podium in such a way that we all knew instinctively that he had much to say about this subject. He expressed his opinion in this way. The comical element simply comes from the fact that a person has the *vis comica*, or the power of being comical [table V]. That would be the same as if an economist were to ask

2. Heinrich Heine, poet, 1797-1856. His statement that "poverty comes from pauperism" could not be documented. A very similar statement can be found in Fritz Reuter's *Out of My Stormy Time*, chapter 38: Inspector Braesig says: "The great poverty in the city comes from the pauperism."

where money comes from and reply that it comes from the power of making money. By saying this, you haven't explained anything at all.

Scholars and experts in the field of economics would immediately think that you were rather strange if you said that the origin of money can be found in the power that creates money. But scientists in the field of natural sciences don't notice anything wrong when someone asks where the enlivening power in milk comes from and is given the answer "from vitamins." But that's just like saying that poverty comes from pauperism. And nobody notices anything wrong. They even think that this person has said something very profound and true, but in reality nothing of significance has been said.

This is what is so upsetting, if I may say so, about the way things are conducted in modern-day science. These scientists think they are saying something truly important. They announce their results using big words, and all the rest of the people believe everything they say. If this type of thing continues in the course of history, the time will come when everything will have to wither and die. For the world is dependent on your ability to actually do something and not only talk about things and create new abstract terms. Words must mean exactly what is really there. Long ago there used to be a kind of science that was directly connected to the actual experience of those things under examination. Today we have a science that knows nothing anymore of this direct experience. All it does is think up fantastic new word combinations, and this is only possible because a new authority has been added to the old one.

You must also consider how recent the proliferation of scientific journals in specialty areas is; there used to be very few such journals. Reports are printed in these journals on experiments involving beekeeping after the beekeepers have met at one of their conferences. This was still so at the time when I was young. Then, after a conference you could still learn how things were. One beekeeper would relate his experiences to another, and you could immediately tell if someone was a windbag or if the person had real experiences to back up the statements. It's a very different matter when you hear a person speak. You can tell if the person is speaking about something he or she knows or is only repeating things heard from others. What has been added to this method is the new authority of having something appear in print. When something is printed, people immediately think there must be something to it, because a printed page lends an air of authority to whatever is being conveyed.

In this article we are talking about, there is an additional element. This doctor has actually bestowed a blessing by conducting her honey cures. In relating these research results, she has accomplished something truly excellent. And now she starts to think about these results as a modern scientist would, and she comes up empty-handed. She even says so:

> It would be desirable to have the results of our experiments publicized far and wide and particularly to ensure that our young people will once again eat more honey. For the present, our report includes only the results of our practical experiences, but we don't doubt that as more knowledge about vitamins is obtained, pharmacologists and physiologists will need to devote attention to the problem concerning the effect of honey upon the entire human organism.

Likewise, the author of this article states at the very beginning:

> I feel called on, at some point, to give a doctor's perspective regarding the effects of the honey cure.... Our successful results encourage me to try to uncover the

deeper relationships and conditions that must exist. Although I am certainly conscious of the fact that I haven't even scratched the surface, I would, nevertheless, like to indicate, based on our experiences and the results of our experiments, the points from which, in my opinion, future research could continue.

Well, from her own words it becomes clear that this doctor has sufficient modesty to say that using all we know today about vitamins, there is no way to get to the core of this matter.

Now here is something you'll want to consider carefully. We'll try to determine the basis for the effects caused by the honey cures. These experiments do show us something. They show us that the effect of honey is particularly strong— the experiments will continue to demonstrate this more and more—not in very young children, but rather in those children undergoing second dentition or in those who have definitely already replaced their baby teeth with an adult set of teeth. It is very important to consider this point, which the results clearly demonstrate. But the results also show that honey has its best effect in children if you dissolve it in moderately hot milk. It is this combination of honey and milk that has a strong effect in children.

If you continue thinking along these lines, you'll find something else to be true. Honey can begin to have a significant effect upon still younger children. But it is important to use a small amount of honey—more milk, but less honey. In older people it is primarily the honey that helps, not the milk. You can obtain favorable results in very old people by allowing them to ingest honey without any milk at all. Based upon the experiences recorded here as the results of experiments, you would have to come to the conclusion that milk and honey play an extraordinarily significant role in the life of a human being.

And, gentlemen, as I've told you before, the older forms of science weren't as primitive and stupid as present-day science would have you believe. These older forms of science often expressed things in a simplistic way, but they were, in reality, very wise in their insights. And you know that the old phrase "This is a country where milk and honey flow" simply means that it is a healthy country, a country where you can live a healthy life. The people of antiquity knew that both milk and honey are strongly connected with a healthy human life force.

Nature sometimes talks to us in a very understandable manner. You will notice what it says if you can take the simple things simply enough. Whoever knows that nature works in very wise ways will not need much proof to determine that milk is something that is good for little children and those who are growing up to adulthood. Otherwise nature would have seen to it that honey, and not milk, would flow from a woman's breast. This is something that is not out of the realm of possibility. Because plants produce honey, it could indeed be possible for the mammary glands of women to produce honey. You simply have to take things on a simple basis. You should not say that nature is a bungler, constantly botching things—but rather say to yourself that behind all of it lies a fact you can recognize, that milk nourishment is the primary concern for a small child, but as the child grows, you can add more and more of the honey nourishment.

We really shouldn't get such an idea in our minds, an idea of the abstract word definition type, and then say to ourselves that poverty comes from pauperism, the comical element from the comic force, and the enlivening force of honey from a vitamin contained in it; on the contrary, we should direct our attention to the reality in these relationships. And in this regard I am going to tell you this—we'll put together some ideas we've already encountered in these lectures, but it will be important for you to be able to look at these things with the proper and correct perspective.

You see, gentlemen, when you go up into the highest parts of the Alps, where these high mountains are the hardest, where, in a sense, the hardest parts of the Earth extrude upward, right there you'll find quartz crystals. They are very beautiful. In general, you will find all sorts of crystals there. Remember how I sketched these quartz crystals for you. They look like this [see drawing, also table V]. When they are complete crystals, they will look as if they are closed off below, just as they are on top. But most of the time they are not complete. They come out of the surrounding rocky material; they seem to grow out of the rock in the way I've already frequently sketched for you. What does this mean? This means that the Earth lets such crystals grow out of itself, crystals that are six-sided and terminate in a point. So within the Earth is a power that can shape something like this so that it will have six sides.

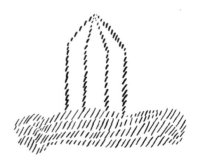

As I've always explained to you, in human beings reside all the forces that are in the Earth as well as in the cosmos. The Earth, in turn, receives this force from the cosmos. Human beings get it from the Earth. The force with which the Earth presses out this quartz crystal is contained in a human being. How is it possible that this power is in us? Well, it's true that the human body is full of quartz.

Now you'll probably say, "That man must really be crazy; listen to that strange rubbish he's telling us!" The quartz you find up there in the mountains is truly a hard substance. You can crack a human skull with it, and nothing happens to the quartz crystal. Its rigidity is one of its most prominent features. But substances do not always have the same form that they present to us here and there. In human beings exists this very same substance that the quartz crystal is made of, but it takes a more fluid form [table VI, page 164]. Why?

You see, it's possible to observe—you simply have to observe properly through a spiritual eye directed inwardly—how there is a constant stream of something from the head into the members of the human body. It is interesting how the same substance the Earth let stream out of itself became hard, took on the form of a quartz crystal, and can now be seen constantly flowing downward from the human head. With the Earth it is found streaming out from the Earth's interior, and with human beings it streams from the head to the rest

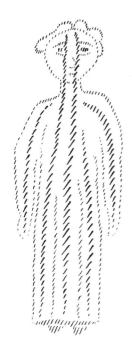

of the body. It is either quartz or silicic acid. The only difference is that the human body doesn't allow the quartz to become crystallized. That would really be something, if we were inwardly completely filled with quartz crystals. That would really hurt! The human body allows the quartz substance to develop up to the point where quartz wants to take on its six-sided shape, and then it stops the process at that very point. The body simply doesn't let it happen.

Our life as human beings is dependent on the fact that we continuously want to form six-sided crystals, beginning with the head and going down into the rest of the body, but we stop this crystal formation just in time, so that it doesn't happen. As a result, we have what you might call a very thin solution of quartz "fluid" in us. If we didn't have this quartz substance in us, we would, for instance, never have a sweet taste in our mouths, no matter how much sugar we ate. The quartz we have in us is responsible for this, not because of its chemical composition but rather by virtue of the fact that it has a strong will to take on a six-sided form as a crystal. This is what does it. Everything depends on our understanding this properly.

So you see, in the Earth we find the same substance, only further developed. The human being stops the process at the point of the development of silicic acid, just when this process wants to become spiky. The Earth allows this process to continue until the sharp-pointed nature of quartz pokes its way through to the surface. But the human being needs and uses this power, this silicic acid power, which is the power to produce these six-sided shapes.

I can imagine that not all of you were good in geometry. Not all of you will have geometry fresh in your minds. You might not immediately be able to sketch a quartz crystal or model it in clay. But your body is a good geometrician. It wants continuously to make such crystals, but we are held back from doing so. All life consists in stopping the process of dying, and when we no longer are able to stop it, then we simply experience the actual death we've been trying to avoid.

Now let's look at a bee again. The bee flies out and collects honey nectar. In its own body it transforms this honey nectar into honey and creates from it its own powers of life. But it also produces wax. What does it do with this wax? It makes six-sided cells from it. You see, the Earth makes six-sided silicic acid crystals, while the bee makes six-sided cells. This is terribly interesting. If I were to sketch for you these cells, or if you can remember how Mr. Müller showed them to you, then you will see that they look like quartz crystals, the only difference being that they are hollow. The quartz crystal is not. But in their form they are completely alike [table VI, upper right].

You see, gentlemen, these cells are hollow. But what goes in there? The egg of the bee is placed into it. Where the silicic acid is contained in the quartz, it is hollow in the cell—

that's where a bee egg is placed. The bee is formed by the same force that resides in the Earth and can construct a quartz crystal. It's the finely distributed silicic acid that has this effect. There is a force in it that can' t be proved using physical methods. In this process the honey, having been worked upon by the bee's body, has such an effect that it can create wax in just such a form that human beings can use, because all human beings need to have these six-sided spaces within themselves. Human beings need the same things bees do. And since the bee is that creature that can best of all create this force of having a six-sided effect on other things, the bee collects from everything available in nature the very form of nourishment that can carry over into our bodies this same hexagonally acting force, a force that produces a six-sided effect.

You see, gentlemen, if you eat honey, you will take into yourselves a tremendously strengthening force. If you have become too weak to develop within yourselves this six-sided force that must flow from your head to the rest of the body, if you don't have any longer the power to give your blood a certain degree of solidity so that this six-sided force is continually present, then honey must step in to make up for the loss, or, in the case of children, milk will be necessary. Children don't have this six-sided force as yet—they still must obtain it through that which a woman produces in herself in the form of milk.

This is why, no matter how much casein, fat, sugar, and salt you give mice to eat, they will still die. Why? Because this animal also needs this force to produce the six-sided effect. Just mixing casein, fat, sugar, and salt is not going to yield real milk because the power that expresses itself in six-sidedness is not there. If you give real milk to mice, this force is imparted; however, it is not contained in milk to such a degree that when the milk turns sour, it will form six-sided crystals. If this hexagonally acting force were just a bit stronger in the milk, then you would be able to drink sour milk that would create tiny silicic acid crystals on your tongue. It would feel as if there were tiny hairs present in the milk. But in milk the crystallization process doesn't ever reach this point, because the milk originates in a human or animal body, where it remains fluid. For a child the power contained in milk is sufficient, but not for an adult human being. This maturation toward adulthood, however, begins in childhood. At that time you need to begin adding the stronger six-sided activating force that is contained in honey.

Another interesting point is this. Milk, even if it comes from a human being, is in reality animal-like in nature; it comes from the animal part of a human being. Thus, in the human being milk is animal. Honey, on the other hand, comes from the plant kingdom via a detour through the bee. Originating in the plant kingdom, it is considered vegetable. Silicic acid, let's say quartz, is mineral. It has a distinct hexagonal shape. The wax, which comes about within the bee as it is influenced by the bee's metabolism, takes on its form—the wax isn't derived directly from the bee's nourishment, but it receives its form from it—and is shaped into a six-sided cell. Milk dissolves this shape or form quickly and allows only a shadowy image of six-sided crystals to be formed [table VI, lower right]. As a result, you can say that honey is that form of nutrition that must have the most salutary and beneficial effects on a human being.

I suppose you could also reason that it would be a good thing for human beings to substitute silicic acid for honey, because the silicic acid would also supply a method for getting this six-sided power into your system. But silicic acid has an effect on human beings that is too strong because it was pushed too far along in the process of attaining a six-sided shape and forming the typical silicic acid shape within itself. Nevertheless, it has some beneficial effects for the human being.

Now assume the following circumstance. Imagine a poor child isn't lucky and doesn't receive a honey cure of the type described in the article at the age of sixteen or seventeen, or even of thirteen or fourteen, when it is best. This child doesn't fare well. The percentage of red corpuscles in the blood is reduced more and more as time progresses. The child grows older and at the age of thirty, let's say, lives in poverty and has become a very weak human being. The writer of the article even says as much when she says, "They simply collapse." But now you have before you a person who is thirty years old. You could easily initiate a honey cure, but this person has become too enervated, too emaciated. In order to help such a person, you would have to give so much honey that the stomach would be spoiled in the process, for honey is something that demands moderation from the human being who eats it. If you eat too much honey, you will upset your stomach.

This is based on a very simple fact. Honey is sweet and contains a lot of sugar. Your stomach, however, needs primarily an acidic content. So when you ingest too many sweet things, you will spoil the acidic effect the stomach is trying to produce. If you gave such an emaciated person who is thirty years old as much honey as such a person would need in order to bring about a positive outcome, he or she would, at first, suffer from indigestion, which would lead eventually to a chronic intestinal condition. You simply can't do it.

You could try something else. You could, to begin with, give such a person, as a medication, a drastically diluted solution containing powdered quartz, which is silicic acid. If you give someone this extremely thin solution of silicic acid as a remedy, this person will, after a certain amount of time has passed, regain the capability of absorbing the beneficial effects of small quantities of honey. This very thinly dissolved silicic acid will have stimulated within the person the power to make use of the hexagonal force. In this way you can use a lesser amount of honey as a follow-up. So the silicic acid can, in a sense, prepare the way for the honey. You could do something similar with a thirty-year-old individual whose hemoglobin content is too low. Add a bit of extremely diluted silicic acid directly to the honey. This is generally permissible for all adults, whereas with children it is best to give them a great deal of milk. In this way the honey can have its effect on human beings.

You must know how all these things are connected. And then you will be able to ask, "What is it, in reality, that brings about the effect that honey can have on human beings?" It's this hexagonal formative force that works via the honey upon the human being. This power is inside the bee. You can see its effects by observing the bee's wax cells. It is through this power that honey can be of such benefit to humans. For this reason, the statement I made to you earlier is true—in a child it is primarily the power in milk that is effective, but you can strengthen this power with honey. With adults, for the most part, it is the power in honey that has a strong effect. When a person gets older and has definitely left childhood behind, you will need to strengthen the power in honey with that contained in quartz, as I have described for you. An adult might still derive some benefit from a honey-milk cure because the powers of early childhood might still be present. A simple honey cure might also be beneficial. The benefits of a honey cure remain incontestable.

Those involved in the practical application of these cures know very well that these beneficial effects exist. What we need to do is make clear to practitioners that they should see to it that the properly measured amounts of honey be available commercially. People generally tend to let themselves be deceived. I don't mean this in the usual criminal sense of the word, but rather I would say that they let themselves be deceived by the general conditions that exist in our culture. If you travel about anywhere and go into hotels where you might ask for some honey, you will frequently receive not honey, but a substitute sugar honey that was produced artificially! If only people knew that such honey isn't the same thing as real honey, that there is no way that this power that produces the hexagonal effect can be present, they could not have the wool pulled over their eyes so that they would believe that this artificially made honey has the same effect that genuine honey has. You could, naturally, feed mice with real honey. They would even enjoy the taste of it. However, if you gave them artificial honey, they would die fairly soon, perhaps even in just a few days. This is what I wanted to say about the article on honey-milk cures.

Now there is another interesting matter that has come to my attention. I would like to speak about it, but also to hear from you as to what your thoughts might be about the matter, as well as from Mr. Müller, who also will speak to you regarding this matter. You'll see that so many questions will come up that we'll have to talk about this again next time. You'll be able then to ask questions, and Mr. Müller or I will answer them. At this time I want only to touch upon two things quickly. These may seem rather strange to you, but I'm quite interested in finding out how you will react to them.

Question submitted in writing: Among the beekeepers in traditional farming communities, there is a conviction that between the beekeeper and the bees, there is a certain soul connection, a spiritual bond that exists between them. So they say that if the beekeeper dies, the death must immediately be made known to the bees. If this is not done, all of the bees will die during the course of the next year. That a certain spiritual rapport exists between them is made clear by the experience that many have had. If you try to attend to your bees when you are in an angry mood, the bees will sting you more frequently than if you carry out your tasks with the bees when you are in a calm mood and in harmony with your environment. Is there any basis in reality for this somewhat ancient notion that older beekeepers have?

Dr. Steiner: It would be interesting to hear from Mr. Müller, if he could simply say that such things are a total figment of the imagination. Such things as announcing the death of the beekeeper are customary among beekeepers in the country. But I'm more interested in this spiritual rapport, this relationship between the beekeeper and the bees. Perhaps Mr. Müller could say something about this.

Mr. Müller: (*Mr. Müller talks about two illustrative cases in Basel and Zurich.*) In one family the wife who had helped very much in tending the bees died, and in the course of one year all of the hives died out. In another case, this one in Basel, it was also a wife who was very much devoted to tending the bees who died. The same thing happened. It was a large apiary. In the course of a year, twenty-eight hives were reduced to only six. I can't explain how that is connected to the time span and why it happened to those bees. In one case it was established that the bees did not die of any known disease; perhaps there was a soul connection.

Dr. Steiner: Let's try to remember what I once told you about the connection between humans and animals. You may have heard me talking about it; I've mentioned it in the past. A while ago there was much talk about so-called calculating horses,[3] horses that were given a question, such as "How much is four plus five?" Then the owner of the horse began counting—one, two, three, four, five, six, seven, eight, nine—at which point the horse stamped the ground with its foot. These horses did innumerable calculations like this. You've probably heard that the horses from the Elberfeld region became quite famous in this regard. Investigative commissions were sent there to research this matter and get to the bottom of it. I myself have not seen these horses from Elberfeld, but I saw another such calculating horse that belonged to a Mr. von Osten. This horse also performed this feat. From this example alone, you could draw a conclusion as to the real basis for such a phenomenon.

People have really racked their brains to try to figure this one out. When you think about it, there is something terribly shocking about horses that are said to suddenly begin doing calculations. They calculate so well that you could

3. See the article by Oskar Pfungst, "Mr. von Osten's Horse, 'Smart John'— A Contribution to Experimental Animal- and Human-Psychology," Leipzig, 1937.

almost dispense with calculating machines. Well, gentlemen, if you could teach horses to do this, the competition between horses on the one hand and bookkeepers and accountants on the other could become fierce. However, the story behind these horses is not a nice one.

Even the scientific world suffered an unbelievable degree of embarrassment in probing for the truth in this matter. There is, however, an easy way to get a handle on it. Naturally, a horse can't really do calculations. What you need to find out is why it happens that the horse stamps its foot at the number nine. It would be a case of complete idiocy to contend, or even believe, that a horse is able to do these calculations. Even Professor Pfungst, who studied this matter very carefully, knew this for a fact. But he then established a theory. He said to himself, "Mr. von Osten must make a certain kind of face or have a slightly different expression on his face, and then the horse must see this slightly changed expression on his face. The horse must detect this very slight change in the lines on his face. When seeing this change, the horse stamps its foot." But then this professor states his own objection to this line of thinking. He figures that he should be able to place himself directly before Mr. von Osten and watch his facial expressions very carefully. This he did, but he noticed nothing at all. But he didn't let himself get confused by his own theory. So he said to himself, "This change in expression is so minute that I can't detect it, but the horse can." Well, gentlemen, what we can conclude from this is that a horse can see more and better than a professor. There can be no other conclusion.

But this is not the way things are. If you are trained in anthroposophic science, which allows for a spiritual as well as the obvious physical dimension, and you go to examine this matter, then you will not place emphasis upon any slight change in expression. But this is the way things really were.

The horse stood on one side and Mr. von Osten, holding the bridle loosely, stood on the other side. And in the right pocket of his jacket, Mr. von Osten had many small pieces of sugar, which he continually gave to the horse. The more the horse licked and ate these pieces and savored their sweetness, the more it began to love Mr. von Osten. As this love increased, supported each time by the offering of sugar, a very cordial relationship between Mr. von Osten and the horse was formed. Mr. von Osten didn't even need to change his expression ever so slightly; he only needed to think, "When I reach nine, the calculation is correct." The horse then senses this thought because animals have a much finer sensitivity to all those things that are going on in their immediate environment. They sense what is going on in your head even though you don't express it visually through a facial expression that a horse might see, but not a human being. The horse senses what is going on in your brain when you are thinking "nine" and then stamps its foot. If the horse had not received the sugar, the horse's love might have transformed itself somewhat into hate and then it would not have stamped its foot.

So you see, animals have a very fine sensitivity for things—not for almost imperceptible facial expressions, but rather for truly invisible things, just as Hans the horse had for what was happening in Mr. von Osten's brain. These are things you simply have to observe; then you will know that animals indeed can feel things in, what seems to us, a very marvelous way.

Just imagine for a moment that you are walking into a swarm of bees and you are extremely afraid. Well, the bees can feel that you have fear; there is no way to deny it. What does it mean that you are afraid? You know that if you are afraid, you will become pale. And when you become pale, your blood is held back. It doesn't flow outwardly into your skin. Now when a bee approaches a person who is afraid, it senses in that person, more than it normally does when the blood is properly distributed in the skin, this force that affects things in a six-sided manner, and it wants to obtain from you honey or wax. Whereas if a person calmly approaches the bees, and the blood is distributed evenly, the bee has a very different experience. The bee then notices that the person's blood has the same amount of the six-sided power as it has.

Now imagine that you are angry as you approach the bees. Anger will make you red. In this case, a lot of blood suffuses the skin, and this blood wants to receive more of the six-sided force. The bee, with its fine sensitivity, notices this and believes that you want to take away from it this six-sided power—so it stings you. These are very fine sensibilities that register the various powers in nature that are playing about out there or are contained inside things.

Add to this the process of becoming accustomed to being in someone's presence. Consider also that a beekeeper doesn't approach a beehive the same way any person, chosen randomly, would walk up to a beehive. The bees feel, if I may use this expression, a person's effluvia, exhalations, vapors, or perspiration. They know what makes up a specific human being and become accustomed to this individual. If this person dies, then they have to break the relationship with one and gradually become accustomed to another. This is of great significance for the bees. Consider what you can find happening with dogs. It has happened before that when the master of a dog died, the dog went to its master's grave and died there because it couldn't easily get used to a new master. So why can't you assume that bees, known for having a very fine sense for chemical substances, can perceive all these things, that they can become so accustomed to a particular beekeeper that they are unable to do an about-face and immediately accept a new beekeeper? There is something very important upon which all of this is based.

But you may say, "Is the situation with dogs and horses the same as with those tiny creatures, the insects?" Well, you may not have observed this, but it is nevertheless true. You can find people who have a green thumb when it comes to growing plants, whether it's potted plants or plants growing outside. Another person puts in at least the same amount of effort—nothing happens. It's a person's *Ausdünstung* (exhalations, vapors, perspiration, and so forth) that influences the flowers favorably when it comes from one person, but unfavorably when it comes from another. And for some individuals, growing plants comes completely to nothing. This unfavorable influence is primarily on the force residing in the plant, a force that produces the nectar and that produces sweetness within the plant. So you could say that human beings can affect flowers, but they can affect bees even more strongly. You don't have to be astonished about this at all; just keep the facts together in their proper relationships. You'll then see that such things can really be true. You'll also be able to consider these matters as you carry out the practical aspects of beekeeping.

Second question: There's an old farmer's saying that states that if it rains on the third of May, the nectar gets washed out of the blossoms on flowers and trees so that honey production is reduced that year. My observations during the past four years seem to indicate there may be some truth to this adage. Is something like this really possible?

Dr. Steiner: Yes, gentlemen, this is something that will lead us more deeply into the area of the various influences that exist in nature. The fact that it is specifically the third of May is of lesser importance. What is important is the season that is active around this time of year. What does it mean, when it rains at this time near the beginning of May? I once told you that the vernal equinox is now located in the constellation Pisces [table V, upper left]. The Sun remains in this constellation until approximately April 23, at which time it moves into the constellation Aries. At the beginning of May, the Sun's rays come from a different part of the sky than they do at other times of the year. Assume, for instance, that the weather is beautiful at the beginning of May, which would include May 3. What does this mean? It means that the Sun exerts a powerful influence upon all earthly things. All those things that happen here on Earth take place under the Sun's influence when the weather is beautiful. What then would be the significance of rain on May 3 or at the beginning of May? It means that the Earth's forces are greater and dispel the effects of the Sun.

All of this is of tremendous importance for the growth of all plants. If the Sun's power can allow its influence to be felt at just that point in time when the Sun's rays originate from the Aries region of the sky, so that it can bring its full force to bear upon the flowers, then the flowers will develop this sweet substance that appears in the nectar. Then the bees will find this nectar to make honey. If, however, the Earth's power can prevail, when there is rain at this time, then the flowers can't develop under the Sun's rays that come from the Aries region, but they will have to wait for a later Sun period, or they may be interrupted entirely in the development of what they already have. Then the flowers will not properly produce nectar, and the bees will not find any honey.

These matters will become clear to you if you know that everything that happens on Earth, as I have frequently told you before, is open to the influences emanating from the cosmos, from whatever is located outside the Earth and surrounds it in all directions. Rain simply means that the Sun's influence is driven away. Beautiful, clear weather means that the Sun's power can manifest its full potential in the influences it sends in the direction of the Earth. And what is important is not that the Sun generally shines in our direction all year long, but rather that the Sun's forces are coming from a specific area of the sky, not the area we are looking at now [December 1] but specifically the region known as Aries. From every corner of the sky, the Sun's power acts differently. It is not the Sun alone that has these effects; instead it is important that the background behind the Sun is a certain region, such as Aries. That which the Aries region gives to the Sun is assimilated by the Sun and then passed on in the Sun's rays. It's quite a different matter if the Sun sends its rays to the Earth at the beginning or at the end of May. At the beginning of May, the full power of Aries is still effective, but at the end of May, the power of Taurus makes itself known. At this point the influence is one that no longer can exert itself on plants in the same way; its effect is rather one that causes the plants to harden and dry out, and, as a result, the plants no longer have the proper power to create nectar [table VI, middle].

So there is, after all, something to these old farmers' sayings. One ought to pay attention to them. Naturally, as I've told you before, the proper understanding of such things has been lost, and for this reason we have become superstitious. This happens when you no longer can distinguish one thing from another. Then these proverbs or adages have about the same value as the one that says: If the rooster crows on the dung heap, either the weather will change or it will remain as it is. But this is not always the case with such sayings. Some of them are based on ancient wisdom, which you will need to delve into. The farmers who followed these sayings sometimes did very well for themselves in adhering to them. You see, a deeper understanding can lead us back to using such sayings, albeit with a new understanding of their significance.

We'll continue next Wednesday.

• Lecture Four

Dornach, December 5, 1923

Mr. Erbsmehl states that beekeepers today are primarily concerned with the profits gained from beekeeping. Every effort is directed toward this materialistic goal. In the Swiss Apiculture Newspaper, *no. 10, October 1923, you will find the following statement: "Honey is, for the most part, a luxury item, and those who purchase it can afford to pay a good price for it." Later on, in the same newspaper, an example is given of a certain Mr. Baldensberger[1] who traveled throughout Spain and, on one occasion, found a group of very healthy children assembled about a beekeeper. He asked the beekeeper, "Whom do you sell your honey to?" The beekeeper immediately replied, "These are my customers." Here in the heart of Europe the goal is to get as much out of the honey as possible. An employer's main interest is to see how much labor can be gotten out of the employees. The same applies also to the bees.*

Another question is posed as to whether there might be any truth to the opinion expressed by some that moonlight has a certain influence on the formation of nectar in flowers (no. 11 of the same newspaper).

Mr. Müller responds that Mr. Erbsmehl can easily see from reading the apicultural newspaper that it can only be a beekeeper with a small number of hives who doesn't sell any honey at all. Mr. Erbsmehl simply doesn't know yet how much is presently involved in a

---

1. Ph. T. Baldensberger, a well-known beekeeper, in *Bulletin de l'Apiculture des Alpes Martimes.*

beekeeping operation and that a certain amount of bookkeeping is necessary. If you don't plan financially for some profit in this venture, just as you would in any other enterprise, then you'd simply have to give up beekeeping. The large quantity of honey available commercially would not be there if you didn't obtain honey that was produced by artificial breeding in this way. Sometimes the yield is only one to two kilos of honey; under certain conditions it even contains some fir tree honey,[2] which you have to remove if you want to keep the bee colonies healthy. That's all.

After that there may be a bad year, and you won't have enough to last until April or May. You'll need to use artificial feeding—sugar, chamomile tea, thyme, and some salt—in order to get the bee colonies through a difficult period so as to maintain them in a state of continuous vitality. In a modern beekeeping operation, you need to keep a record of how much time the beekeeper has worked, five- and-one-half hours at the going rate of 1 or 1.5 Swiss francs. Then the honey would have to be sold at a price of 7 Swiss francs. You can also count on losses; you may lose the framework for the honeycomb and then have to replace something. The whole thing has to turn a profit. If a beekeeper were only to stick to the old way of doing things, then the beekeeper wouldn't make any progress. Mr. Erbsmehl can do that with his small operation, but if you have a large number of hives, then you have to sit down and figure out that you have already incurred a deficit when you ask 6 Swiss francs. The American beekeepers do it the same way.

Mr. Müller cannot comprehend that the bee colonies may die out in eighty or one hundred years. He simply can't understand how Dr. Steiner can say that, in fifty or one hundred years, artificial breeding can cause serious problems for the bee colonies to which it has been applied.

In regard to the second point about announcing the death of the beekeeper to the bees, he already mentioned that the greatest portion of

---

2. *Fichtenhonig* (*Waldhonig*) is honey from the honey-dew that aphids secrete.

the hives died out when the beekeeper who tended them died. Just how this can happen, he simply can't comprehend.

About the adulterated or artificially made honey in hotels, he wants to add that first-class hotels are, in many instances, selling American honey. If you feed European bees this honey, which is, after all, a bee product, they die.

Then there is this matter about the bees' stinging: Perspiration is about the worst thing for bees, and if you hear whistling, rattling, or any strident sound, it is advisable to remain standing and not move.

And then with reference to the question that asks about the effect of a bee sting on a human being, he relates one example that he knew about personally. A strong man was stung by a bee. He cried out, "Hold me, I've been stung by a bee!" He was extraordinarily sensitive (allergic) to bee stings. He also had heart disease. He suggests that Dr. Steiner could explain how a bee sting can pose such a great danger to certain human beings. There is, for example, a saying: If a horse is stung three times by hornets, the horse will die. Some time ago, in one of his hives, he says he found a hornets' nest. He simply removed the brood. The hornets were so cowardly that they didn't sting in the dark. Outside they probably would have done so.

Dr. Steiner: Let's investigate, so that we can discuss this matter rationally, how bees can recognize the beekeeper who tends them. You passed judgment on this matter based on your normal understanding of such things, and this is completely justified. But now I want to tell you something. Imagine that you have a friend with whom you became acquainted in, let's say, 1915 [table VII, page 164]. This friend remains here in Europe, and you go to America and return again in 1925. Your friend, let's assume, lives in Arlesheim, where you happen to see him and recognize him and remember who he is. But what has happened meanwhile? I've already explained this to you in detail before on another occasion. All the material substances in the human body are completely renewed or replaced in a period of seven or eight years. The old substances, such as cells, are completely exchanged for new ones. Nothing of that which once was there is there later. So you can say that your friend, if you see him once again after ten years, has none of the physical substances within himself that he once had when you saw him ten years ago. But you recognized him nevertheless. And if you look at him externally, he does appear to you as that same interrelated mass of substances. Yes, he does appear familiar in this way, but if you were to examine him using a sufficiently large magnifying glass, then you would see that [table VII, upper middle] somewhere in his head blood flows through an artery, and when this blood is magnified to a certain point, [table VII, upper right] it no longer looks like blood but rather like many tiny dots that resemble small animals. These tiny dots are constantly quivering and trembling. When you look at this, you will see a great similarity between it and a horde of bees swarming about!

A human being has the appearance of a swarm of bees when you magnify sufficiently the substances contained in the body. Once you've gained a proper insight into all of this, then it would have to seem incomprehensible that one human being could recognize another after ten years, because not a single one of these tiny moving points is still there. His eyes now have completely new "dots." There are new, different little animals in there, and yet a human being will recognize another after a long separation.

It isn't absolutely necessary for these individual tiny "animals" and "plants" of which we consist to be responsible for doing something that makes it possible for us to recognize each other again after a long separation, but it is rather due to the fact that we recognize the whole person. Likewise, the beehive isn't simply what you would call a collection of an undetermined number of bees, but rather a complete whole, a complete being. That which you can recognize again, or not recognize again, is the entire beehive.

If you could zoom out rather than zoom in, you could see all these bees at once and connect them in what would resemble a human muscle. With bees, this is the very thing you must pay attention to: that the object of our concern has nothing to do with the individual bees but rather with that which absolutely belongs together to make up the whole. This is something that a simple understanding of the matter can't fathom. In this case you must be able to view the whole as it must really be. That is why we can learn so much from a beehive or things like it, because a beehive completely contradicts the thoughts we may form about it. Our thoughts keep trying to tell us that the explanation must be different. However, in a beehive the most wonderful things happen. It isn't the way our common understanding of the matter tells us. So, what happens when the change brought about by the death of the beekeeper affects the beehive in a certain way, this can't be denied. It simply happens this way, experience tells us. Someone who is not restricted to one beekeeping operation but sees many such operations is able to observe this as a fact.

I can tell you, for example, that as a boy I had numerous personal experiences relating to beekeeping, and at that time my interest in this matter was extremely great, not because of any connection beekeeping had to economic or commercial questions that interested me after I grew up but rather because honey was prohibitively expensive at that time, so that my parents, who were poor, could never afford to buy any. Whatever honey we had came from our neighbors, usually for Christmas, but we received so much throughout the winter that we had enough honey for the entire year. At that time I wasn't interested in the economic question regarding honey, since I ate almost exclusively honey that had been given as a present. How can this be? Nowadays, under the same conditions, you would not so easily receive honey as present. But back then, in the surrounding area where my parents lived, the beekeepers were primarily farmers who had made beekeeping part of the entire agricultural operation.

This is quite a different situation compared to an individual purchasing whatever a beekeeping operation requires, and add to this the fact that such a person usually is a salaried worker who has to live entirely from hourly wages. In an agricultural operation, beekeeping is carried on in such a way that you don't even notice it. Hardly any consideration is even given to the length of time spent in this activity, because it is something that the farmer somehow manages to find time to do. In farming there is always something that is left over to do. The time spent on such a job may be saved elsewhere, or perhaps a certain task, for some reason, is scheduled for a different time, thereby freeing one up to do something else. In any case, the hives were tended somewhere in between other chores back then, and the people knew that honey was something so valuable you couldn't even pay for it. And this, in a certain sense, is absolutely right, because, under the present economic conditions, everything you can buy suffers from an improper relationship of price as related to the actual work done. Today we really ought not to be discussing these false price relationships, because such a discussion must really be placed upon a much broader basis of political economy. You'll not gain much of an insight if you treat honey as just another item on a grocery list rather than a luxury item like coffee, tea, or chocolate. If the organization of a society were a healthy one, then, without a doubt, a proper price for honey would be established.

It is just because we are not living under healthy social conditions that all the questions we raise will be tainted by the situation we are part of. You see, here is the situation today when you visit large farms. Yes, gentlemen, what the agricultural manager—usually this person is not a farmer, but an accountant-type manager—says to you about the quantity of milk obtained from cows is horrible. The manager gets so many liters of milk a day from a single cow. Anyone who really understands the nature of a cow knows that it is impossible that you can get this much milk from a cow. But they manage somehow to get this amount. As far as I know, some of them have pushed this amount to be double that which a cow can normally give. This brings in a good profit for the farm naturally. And to top it off, you can't even say that you would be able to notice that the milk doesn't have the same nutritional value as the milk that is produced under natural conditions. You can't even prove that something really bad has happened to it.

But let me give you the following example. Over the past few years, we have done many experiments with a medication used to treat hoof-and-mouth disease in cattle.[3] These experiments were conducted on large farms as well as small ones, where the milk production for each cow was lower. You could find out all sorts of things because you had to try out the medication. The experiments were not completed because, officially, the people didn't want to comply with all aspects and because today so many concessions have to be made. But the medication produced some extraordinary results. In a somewhat changed form it is used as a medication to treat canine distemper.

When you do these experiments, you'll discover the following. Calves born to cows that are forced to produce too much milk are considerably weaker. You can observe this in

3. Regarding this remedy, see Joseph Werr's *Animal Husbandry and Animal Medicine in the Framework of Bio-Dynamic Agriculture*, Stuttgart, 1953.

the effect the medication has on the calf. The effectiveness or lack of effectiveness is greatly magnified. Eventually the calf grows up, if it doesn't die of the disease. But a calf whose mother has been overfed in order to force it to give more milk is a much weaker calf than one whose mother was not forced to produce as much milk. You can observe this in the first, second, third, and fourth generations. Then the calf gets to be so small that you hardly notice it. This type of forced milk production has not been in existence for very long, but I know one thing very well, that if people continue along this path, if a single cow is made to deliver over thirty liters of milk a day, if they continue to mistreat these animals this way, then, after some time, dairy farming may come to a bitter end. There's nothing that can be done about that.

Well, to be sure, things are naturally not quite so bad with the artificial feeding and breeding of bees. This is mainly so because the bee is an animal that always knows how to help itself, since it is much closer to nature than a cow, which really can't help itself very much when it is raised and treated in this way. And this ability to help itself out of difficult situations is a truly wonderful thing about a beehive. Now we're getting to the point that Mr. Müller made about the hornets he sometimes finds inside his hives, hornets that don't sting him, whereas any other time a person meets up with a hornet, terrible things can happen.

I also want to tell you something else. I don't know if you've had this experience yourself—those of you who are beekeepers will know about this—but it can happen that you find yourself in a situation that forces you to empty out the entire hive. Well, once I looked into such an empty hive and saw something rather strange there. It looked like a tuber [draws on blackboard, see table VII, lower right]. No one really knew what it was. The bees seemed to have made this tuber for no reason at all. It was made of all the usual substances that bees are capable of producing. Looking like a stone, this tuber consisted of resins, waxes, and glue-like substances. Yes, gentlemen, I was truly curious about what was going on in there, and when I took the tuber apart—lo and behold, a dead mouse was inside!

This mouse had gotten into the hive and died there, and then imagine how terrible the stench of the rotting corpse of the mouse must have been for the bees! In this very extraordinary case, the entire hive had the instinct to surround this dead mouse with a shell. When we took apart the surrounding shell, there was really a terrible smell that had remained inside it until that moment. As you can see, in the whole hive there was not only an instinct to build cells, and to feed the young, but also an instinct to do something when an event so unusual happens, like a mouse entering a hive. Since they were unable to remove the mouse from the hive, they helped themselves by creating a shell around it. I've heard from other beekeepers about snails and slugs that managed to get into the hive and were encrusted there. Alive within the hive are not only the usual instincts but also instincts that help to heal. These are particularly effective.

Well, if a hornets' nest is inside the hive, then the bees do not create such a solid structure, but they continually surround this nest with a secretion of their poison, and for this reason the hornets lose the energy, the power even to attempt to escape. As with the dead mouse, which no longer creates a stench in all directions, the hornet, even though it hasn't been encrusted in a shell, lives continually in the poisonous vapors with which the bees surround themselves so that the hornet becomes weak and can do them no harm. In this way the hornet eventually loses its power and energy, and it can no longer defend itself if you approach it.

You will get on well with bees only if you go beyond the normal, basic understanding of things and actually begin to follow matters with an inner eye. The picture of things you get in this way is indeed wonderful. Using this type of insight, you'll have to say that a beehive is a total entity. You must try to understand it in its totality. And with such an entity the potential damage is not at all noticeable right away.

Whoever knows human beings well, knows, for instance, that one sixty-five- or sixty-six-year-old individual still might have a rather fresh appearance, but another may not be as healthy in appearance because the second one suffers from hardening of the arteries or something like that. To observe this fact and to make a connection between what happened in childhood and later adulthood is extremely interesting. You can, for example, give a child milk that comes from cows that derive too much of their nourishment from plants growing in a soil with a high lime content. In this way the child assimilates, through the cow's milk it drinks, some of the calcium present in the calcareous soil. This calcium intake probably will not manifest itself immediately. Along comes a medical doctor of the modern-day sort and shows you one such child who was raised on milk from a cow that had grazed on land with a predominant lime content and another child who had received only mother's milk, and such a doctor says, "It doesn't make any difference which type of milk the child gets." But it turns out that the child raised on mother's milk is still fresh in appearance at an age of sixty-five or sixty-six, and the other, raised on cow's milk, has suffered from calcification at the same age.

Such a thing happens because a human being is a complete entity, and whatever is effective at a given time may still have aftereffects at a much later time. Something might be quite healthy at one time, but it will still show aftereffects later. And this is just what I'm trying to say. There is no way, based on the current situation with the artificial methods used in feeding and breeding bees, to predict what the significance of these procedures will mean for the future fifty or sixty years, or even a century from now. The fact that someone will say, "I don't understand how things like this would be any different in fifty, sixty, or one hundred years from now" certainly is understandable. This inability to understand, or lack of desire to gain a deeper insight—this is just what I observed once on a large farm. You can rest assured, they really discouraged me in a very friendly manner when I began to talk about reducing the amount of milk taken from each cow. Dairy farming will suffer much faster; it will probably approach a ruinous state in a quarter of a century.

Today it is impossible to object in any way to the artificial methods applied in beekeeping. This is because we live in social conditions that do not allow anything else to be done. Nevertheless, it is important to gain this insight—that it is one matter if you let nature take its course and only help to steer it in the right direction when necessary, but it is entirely another matter if you apply artificial methods to speed things along. But I really don't want to take a strong position against what Mr. Müller has stated. It is quite correct that we can't determine these matters today; it will have to be delayed until a later time. Let's talk to each other again in one hundred years, Mr. Müller; then we'll see what kind of opinion you'll have at that point. This is something that can't be decided today.

Mr. Erbsmehl indicates once again that with beekeepers today, everything they do is based upon profit.

Dr. Steiner: The more you find that somebody is involved in beekeeping as a sideline, the more such a person will have the same opinion that the Spaniard you mentioned had. Well, today this will probably no longer be a common situation, but fifty or sixty years ago a farmer did not regard with any particular value what was collected from the bees. It was always something the farmer didn't count on. The honey was given away for free, or if it was actually sold, the farmer would put the money in the children's piggy banks or something like that. Today conditions have become quite different from what they once were. How could you imagine that someone whose wages are based upon working by the hour or who talks about circumstances in terms of time being money would not be primarily interested in profit? Such individuals arrive at this attitude through all the conditions under which they live. It's true, is it not, that these days there are hobby beekeepers who must interrupt their salaried work and take a vacation without pay in order to conduct their beekeeping activities properly? Then they sit down and calculate into their honey price the money they lost from their normal salaried position.

Just imagine—beekeeping is so old that no one can provide any physical proof of the way it was prior to the domestication of bees. For the most part, people know only about our bees, the European honeybee; their only acquaintance is with the domesticated bee. In natural history textbooks you can even find the type of bee found throughout Europe referred to as the *common house-bee*.[4] It is truly remarkable that people know only of the domesticated bee and have no idea what conditions were like when these bees were found in a wild, natural state, entirely exposed to the forces of nature. We can assume that the domestication of bees reaches very far back into history. As you begin to discuss such ancient matters, consider that the prices of things were very different from those that prevail today. Just remember that people today work in jobs that you can trace back to the time when they originated. But here you

---

4. This term was first used by Alfred Brehm in *Brehm's Illustrated Animal Life*, vol. 3, Leipzig, 1875, p. 474.

have two types of price formation. With bees this goes back to very ancient antiquity. There are no ancient recorded prices to compare with today's prices, as in the metal and lumber industries, which have price lists going back a number of decades. Only when healthy social conditions once again prevail will the proper price of honey arise in accordance with the new and different conditions existing at that future time.

Most people simply have no idea nor can they imagine how difficult it is to discuss price formation or how prices are fixed. In order to talk about these matters, you need a very thorough understanding of the actual conditions that exist. Recently I had an interesting experience that I want to tell you about, because it may cause you to wonder about price formation. A university professor[5] I know wrote a book about political economy. He gave me a copy of the book while I was on a lecture tour. I stayed in one place for two or three days and had time to talk to him, and I told him that I would look at the book but, naturally, not read it entirely. Well, I looked at the book and told him the following: "I've noticed that you have included an index, something that normally repels me, but in this case I found it very helpful. This index contains, of course, a list of subjects you've discussed in the book. Well, I immediately look up the word *price* and, would you believe it, there was nothing at all on that subject."

How can this educated man write a book on political economy and not include anything in it on the subject of price? Yes, gentlemen, this is very typical. Today, political economists are not even capable of seeing the most important problem in political economy. They simply omit the problem of price formation. It is very important, but people don't seem to recognize it. When a thing like this happens, it becomes even more apparent that something is wrong. In

---

5. Reference could not be determined.

this case you will simply have to hope that little by little people will come to the conclusion that healthier social conditions must be initiated. Then, I think, there will not be so much concentration on the profit motive, the bottom line. These are concepts that are connected with the idea of competition; it may not necessarily be the competition between those who make similar products but rather between those who produce different products.

If you were to look back into my youth and examine beekeeping practices in the region where I lived, where only farmers tended bees—well, those farmers were rather corpulent. I can't even say that anyone here is as fat as those farmers were. The price of honey was of such a nature that no one would have even considered beekeeping as a sole occupation, in order to sell honey for money. If the beekeeper had placed himself next to the farmer, it would have looked like this [drawing below, see also table VII, middle]—this would be the farmer and that the beekeeper.

It simply wouldn't have worked out! The farmer wouldn't have had to include the cost of beekeeping in his expenses, whereas the beekeeper would have. This situation would have been intolerable. This is why it is so important to understand political economy and include it in your considerations when you start talking about making a profit.

Now I'd like to answer a few questions about the subjects we have just discussed.

Someone says that there are some people who simply can't tolerate any honey at all. They immediately suffer from heartburn and indigestion. Is there any medication that might control this negative effect of honey?

Dr. Steiner: People of the type that can't tolerate any honey are usually those who tend toward getting sclerosis, an inclination toward hardening throughout the entire body, which causes the body's metabolic rate to be quite slow. This is why they can't tolerate honey, the primary effect of which is to increase the metabolic rate. Within their bodies a split in their metabolism occurs when their bodies want an abnormally slow metabolism and the honey makes it faster. As a result, they get indigestion, which manifests itself in a number of different ways. Every person should be able to enjoy eating some honey, by that I mean not only to enjoy the honey but to have the inner ability to digest it properly. If you have before you people who can't tolerate honey, you should, above all, determine the causes or origins of these conditions. You shouldn't be thinking of finding a general cure or a single medicinal remedy, but rather you must attempt to determine on an individual basis how a person came to develop such a sclerotic condition and then base the cure upon this knowledge. The following case might serve as an example.

Say, for instance, someone is unable to tolerate honey and gets indigestion when attempting to eat it. You need to ask yourself whether this person experiences indigestion when eating honey because the individual tends toward hardening of the arteries, veins, and blood vessels in the head, which is called a head sclerosis. It is possible that at a certain age, such a person will not be able to tolerate honey. In a case such as this, the cure will be effected by giving a preparation containing phosphorus. Then the person will begin tolerating honey, if you can bring about a cure in this way.

But it can also happen that you'll notice that the sclerotic condition is in the lungs. Then you'll need to use, not a preparation containing phosphorus, but one containing sulfur. This is what I wanted to say about this matter. It is important not to lump all these conditions together and to ask a general question about how to treat someone who gets indigestion from honey but rather to say to yourself that if someone can't tolerate honey at a given age, it is evidence of illness. A healthy person can tolerate honey without any problems. If someone doesn't tolerate it, that person is ill, and you must seek the nature of the illness and cure it. Not to be able to tolerate honey isn't as serious as not being able to tolerate sugar, such as in the condition of *diabetes mellitus.* This type of diabetic condition is, naturally, much more serious than not being able to tolerate honey. A diabetic person is truly ill, and you need to treat this illness.

Someone asks, "Just like most insects, bees fly out of the darkness toward the light of a candle lamp. Some experienced beekeepers have told me repeatedly that bees react much less toward electric light. If you approach bees with a flashlight, they remain very calm, as if they don't even see this light. Only after some time has passed do they become restless. Petroleum lamps and candlelight attract them faster and also in greater numbers. Is there an explanation for this behavior?"

Mr. Müller states that he has observed the same reactions.

Dr. Steiner: Well, gentlemen, you may have observed in the first Goetheanum, before it was destroyed by fire that the insides of the domes were painted in various colors. These colors were made from pure, natural plant substances. As a result, these same colors, had they been exposed to sunlight shining in, would have faded and become pale after a certain period of time, perhaps months or even years. Then you would not have seen what had been painted there. If you had exposed them to electric light, they would have remained. So the painters painted with this in mind.

You can also see that sunlight, which has the ability to bring about chemical changes—and you said that the bee notices this—has a very different effect than electric light does. Electric light has much more of a hardening effect on all substances, it doesn't dissolve or break apart substances as sunlight does. Because of this, a bee experiences a very slight rigidity, or paralysis, when exposed to electric light, a reaction it does not have in sunlight. Of course, it quickly recovers from this condition. That's what I wanted to say about that.

Someone asks, "With regard to the influence that the signs of the zodiac can have on the production of honey, in some older, traditional farming communities, the farmers still pay close attention to this, for instance, when they sow the seed, they do so when the moon is in Gemini and so on. Are they superficially following the characteristics of the signs of the zodiac, or is there something else that might be meaningful?"

Dr. Steiner: Things of this type are naturally never properly examined in a scientific manner these days, even though it is possible to do so. I've already indicated to you what has an influence on the beehive. A bee, and specifically the queen, is to a certain degree a "sun" animal. As a result, the sun, as it moves through the zodiac, has the greatest influence upon bees. The changes the sun undergoes as it moves through each sign are transmitted to the bee. But the bees are, naturally, also dependent on that which they find in plants. And this is where there is a connection between the farmers' sowing of the seed under a certain sign of the zodiac and the bees' finding of substances the plants have prepared for them. Such things aren't simply pulled out of nowhere; however, the way they are normally presented is very amateurish and misleading. These matters must be properly examined in a scientific manner so that they will have a firm foundation.

With that we've used up the time allotted to us today. Whatever still remains to be discussed, we'll take up again next Saturday at nine o'clock.[6] I can imagine that many of you will still have questions to bring up at that time. Beekeeping is such a beautiful and useful endeavor that there is no way that one can ask too many questions about it. Ask questions among yourselves, and ask Mr. Müller and me. I think we'll be able to find a way to build a bridge between the differing opinions. We don't have to resort immediately to stinging the way bees do; we can settle these differences in a gentle and friendly atmosphere. But we shouldn't hold back with our questions either.

---

6. This announced lecture actually took place on Monday, December 10, 1923.

• Lecture Five

Dornach, December 10, 1923

Mr. Dollinger asks about honeycombs. There are people who eat the wax of the honeycomb along with the honey. Long ago innkeepers sometimes used to put honeycombs on the table along with the food. He would like to know if there are any detrimental effects that might arise from eating the entire honeycomb. With regard to the diseases that can afflict bees, he thinks that these diseases were not as virulent as they are today, at a time when a larger quantity of honey is taken from the bees and artificial methods are used for feeding and breeding bees.

Mr. Müller says that eating honeycombs is a matter of personal preference. Of course, they need to be of the completely natural type and not those that are artificially constructed. With regard to the diseases that afflict bees, he does not think they arise from modern methods used in working with bees and extracting larger amounts of honey. It is more likely that such diseases simply were not noted as carefully. Also, there were not as many hives with very small populations, so people did not pay as much attention to these things. There is one bee disease that came into Switzerland from England, a disease that had never been here before.

Mr. Erbsmehl thinks that a possible cause might be the use of artificial, chemical fertilizers. Flowers show the negative effects that they can cause.

Dr. Steiner: With regard to both of the things you just mentioned, I might add another point. It's very true that eating the wax comb along with the honey is a type of predilection or penchant that some people have. With such things, it is naturally important to decide how well they can digest it. But that is a question that would have to be answered medically. It would be possible to say something meaningful about this question only if you could observe the people who eat both the honey and the wax comb and then examine their health. I admit that I'm acquainted with various people who do this, but they usually spit out the wax portion after they have extracted the honey in their mouths. But not having observed people who have ingested larger quantities of wax along with the honey, I simply have nothing to report.

There is one thing I suppose you could say. Human beings can tolerate and digest various things, and not everyone the same things. There may be people who, by ingesting beeswax, could develop an unpleasant stomach illness; they, of course, should be advised not to eat the wax. There may be others who would have no problem digesting the wax and who pass the indigestible portions in the stool. In the case of the latter individuals, it would be possible to say that because they also ingest the wax, thereby leaving the honey in contact with the wax as long as possible as it makes its way through the digestive tract, they digest the honey mainly in the intestines, whereas the honey otherwise, under normal conditions, continues being digested in the lymph ducts and so on after it has left the intestines. Well, you could say that this all depends on what state of health the individual is in. There are those who digest more in the intestinal region and others who do it more in the lymph ducts. You won't be able to say simply that one method is good and the other bad; everything must be adjusted to fit the individual human being. You could say something for certain only if you had one group of individuals eat honey with the comb and another honey without it and then determine the relationship between these two groups.

With reference to the diseases that afflict bees, for that matter even diseases in general, you will need to consider what Mr. Müller has said. With humans also it is true that people did not pay any attention at all to certain things, but now they study these things very carefully and pay careful attention to them.

Another essential element also plays a role in this matter. Long ago, a beekeeper did many things based purely on instinct, without really knowing why. Today humankind has lost these instincts, and everybody wants to know the reasons for every little thing. It's just for this reason that it's necessary to investigate every matter very thoroughly, and our present-day method of accumulating knowledge scientifically is usually not capable of doing such a thing. The beekeeper in the past had a very strong instinct to treat the bees in a very, if I may say so, personal and proper manner. Consider, for instance, the difference in providing housing for the bees. In earlier days skeps were provided, but now it is boxes. These boxes are made of wood. Wood is a very different material from that which the "basket"-beehives were made of—plaited straw or similar materials. In addition, this straw, by its nature, attracted from the air very different substances than wood does. So there we already see a difference in the way beekeepers externally treat bees.

If I could summarize for you all the things a beekeeper did in the past, then I would say that there was a strong instinct for the ways things were done. Sometimes the beekeepers did not know at all why they did things in a certain way, but they would select a place for the hives where the wind would reach them from this or that side, or something similar to that. Today these placements are made primarily from practical considerations, such as whether there is room enough for all the hives. Some thought is given to climatic conditions, but not as strongly as in former times.

Mr. Müller says that he still pays considerable attention to these things. He has his apiary on a ridge of hills where there is almost no north wind and not much east wind, and other considerations like that.

Dr. Steiner: Wood is less sensitive to such external elements compared with straw. Don't misunderstand me. I'm not a propagandist for the old-fashioned straw beehives, but these differences exist and also have a strong effect on things, such as the bee, when it accomplishes through inner work all the necessary chemical transformations. In the process of collecting nectar and converting it into honey, the bee carries out a tremendous task within its body. This is truly a gigantic task that the bee needs to complete, and how does it do this? It comes about because of the relationship between two types of juices in the bee: gastric and blood. If you examine the contents of a bee, you'll see the white gastric juice and the somewhat reddish blood juice. These are the two essential components that make up a bee; all the other parts arise out of the effects created by these two juices.

What's really important is that there is a very specific relationship between the gastric juice and the blood juice. There is a significant difference between them. The gastric juice is sour; it is what chemists call *acetous*. The blood juice is what chemists call *alkaline*, which means that it is not *acetous* nor is it an acid, but it can only be acidified. If the gastric juice doesn't have sufficient acid content, then a process takes place within the bee, a process that disturbs its inner organism as honey is being made. The blood juice is strengthened only when the corresponding and very necessary conditions of climate, light, warmth, and so forth are present.

If you want to gain control over such bee diseases as those that have appeared recently, it will depend in large part on bringing about the appropriate effect by regulating and attaining the properly balanced relationship between the bee's gastric and blood juices. And because beekeeping is no longer conducted on such a simple basis as it once was long ago, you won't be able to effect a change through climatic and warmth conditions, since they don't affect the newer beehives. All that is left, then, is to do research to determine what might have the greatest effect on the bee's blood juice. And probably future beekeepers will always need to monitor their bees and make certain that the suitable preparation of the bees' blood juices is constantly taking place. In order to do this, it is important to keep the following point in mind.

It is true, isn't it, that there are years when bees are forced to collect almost all their honey nectar from trees?[1] During such years, the constitution of the bees' blood is in extreme danger; they contract diseases more easily than in other years. For such a situation, it will be important for future beekeepers to set up a very small greenhouse—it doesn't have to be very large—in which the beekeeper will keep and tend artificially such plants that bees love at certain times of the year, plants that bees definitely need. In this way the beekeeper will have a small bed of flowers toward which he can send his bees, for instance, in May. The bees will seek them out by instinct, when those specific plants that they need are either doing very poorly in nature or are not even present during such a period in May.

In this way, by helping nature through placing a small nursery garden in the vicinity of the beehive, you will be able to gain control over such diseases in the future. I would recommend such methods, but they are only suggestions. I do believe they will be worthwhile, since they come from

---

1. What is meant is: from the sugary excretions (honey-dew) of the aphids. See also note on p. 66.

knowledge about the nature of bees. A beekeeper will see good results if these methods are employed. This is the way to fight these diseases, but you'll have to take into account all the relationships that exist in order to proceed in a practical manner.

This is not just my opinion but rather the result of studying the nature of bees. Someone ought to try to set up an experiment with greenhouse plants that thrive at a certain time of year when in nature they are withering or dying off, and probably the bees' health will be improved. I am convinced such effects will come to light when researchers once again investigate these matters with a true cognizance of nature. Today it can no longer be a question of turning back the clock of history. Just as we don't need to be reactionaries in political life, likewise we don't have to be reactionaries in specialized areas. We need to go along with progress. What is important is to pay attention to what we do as we're leaving the old behind, to bring about a balance by means of something else that returns and gives back to us what we've lost. That's what I have to say about this matter.

Mr. Müller states that beekeepers are already working toward providing such artificial plantings dedicated to the purpose just discussed. For example, some have planted yellow crocuses and other similar plants with small, yellow blossoms, in order to make these flowers available to the bees. Many have even planted American clover, which can grow as high as two meters and has blossoms all year long. The farmers wait until fall to harvest it, but before the harvest it is available to the bees. That's what would be necessary.

Dr. Steiner: Yes, they're starting to do these things, but they understand too little about the actual relationships involved. The point that you mentioned first is a good step in the right direction, a direction that should be continued. That which you mentioned about American clover, with its perpetual blossoming, is something that will eventually be abandoned because it doesn't improve the bees' blood juice. What American clover does is stimulate the bees for a short time, just as you might stimulate a human being with alcohol. The bees get all worked up and are able to work harder for a time. But one thing you should watch very carefully. Don't introduce something completely foreign to the bees, since bees, according to their inner nature, have become accustomed to and are tied to a specific area or region. You can see this by noting the variations in the appearance of bees that come from different regions.

There is the middle European bee, the common house bee already mentioned. The Italian bee has a very different appearance; the Carniolan bee is very different from the Italian bee. Bees are very strongly attached to the region they belong to, and as a result you won't be able impart any long-term benefit by giving them nectar derived from regions foreign to them. If you do this, they will need to expend extra energy in converting the nectar within their bodies, where they will experience turmoil as they attempt to convert the nectar into a form like the form it takes in the place the clover came from. For a few years, you might be successful, but there will be real trouble later on. You correctly said that we still don't have enough data to make any meaningful statement about this situation. But time will tell, and beekeepers will stop doing it, or they will do what winegrowers once did.

The experience of the winegrowers was this. You probably know that in the 1870s and 1880s the vine louse (*phylloxera*) suddenly appeared and devastated the vines over large areas of Europe. At that time I was able to occupy myself very thoroughly with this problem because I had as a good friend a farmer who published an agricultural newspaper and devoted much space to this specific problem.[2] There were people who were contemplating why it was that American grapevines had no lice and were not endangered. What came of all this? They discovered that the means used to battle lice on American vines wouldn't work when applied to European vines. The result was that when they began planting the American vines, they were successful in keeping the American vines healthy, but the European ones still died. Then they were forced to give up the European vines entirely and Americanize the entire process of growing grapes. Thus viticulture became entirely transformed and evolved into something very different from what it once was. In many regions it has become something very distinct in many ways. You can't think so mechanically about it, but you should be clear in your minds that things, by their very nature, are tied to certain localities because they have become accustomed to them. This must be taken into consideration. Otherwise you can probably achieve momentary successes, but not anything lasting.

Is there anything else you would like to ask, or are all the silent gentlemen interested only in eating honey, but not in engaging in much discussion about it? Perhaps one or the other of you will think of something that you could ask! I would still like to revisit the matter concerning the true nature of the bee's ability to create honey and fill in a few more details. Basically, it is truly a wonderful thing that such small creatures exist that are capable of extracting from

---

2. Most probably this was Hugo Hitschmann, 1838-1904, founder of modern newspapers on forestry and agriculture in Austria. He co-founded governmental organizations on forestry and agriculture and, after 1870, owned the *Viennese Agricultural Newspaper*. In 1883 he established the *Austrian Forestry and Hunting Newspaper*; in 1884 the *General Wine Newspaper*; in 1867 the *Practical Farmer*; and in 1878 the *Economist*. Beginning in 1879, he also published *A Farmer's Pocket Calendar* and, beginning in 1882, *Archive for Farming Matters* and *A Handbook for the Farmer*.

blossoms, flowers, and plants that substance which they transform into this extraordinarily healthy honey, a substance that could play a more important role in human nutrition than it does today. All that is necessary is that people gain a thorough insight into how terribly important honey is as a food. For example, if it were possible to exert more of an influence on the entire field of what I might call "social" medicine, I would consider it an extremely favorable influence if couples, during the time of their engagement, would eat honey as a preparatory activity before having children. For in this way they would not have rickety children, because there is in honey a force that can affect the reproductive power in human beings, who then, in turn, transform this honey power further so as to give the offspring a proper bodily form. The parents'—more specifically, the mother's—consumption of honey has a beneficial effect that extends itself to the bony, skeletal frame of the child.

Such influences will be discovered once people investigate the deeper connections between these things. Rather than all these useless details and vagaries that you can encounter printed in scientific journals today, you'll find, at some point in the future, when they know something about these matters, such questions as "Which foods are considered good nutrition at such and such a time in life, and which are good at another time of life?" and so on. Yes, that will be of tremendous use to people, because their condition of health will be vastly improved as a result of it; more particularly, their level of energy will increase. The one thing you can say is that people generally do not attach very much value to these facts, because a person who doesn't have rickety children may, to be sure, be very happy about it, but would not really think about it very much. It is accepted as a matter of course without much attention being paid to it. The only person who complains is the one who has rickety children. Hence, I would like to say that those very medical-social regulations that are the most useful have to wait the longest before becoming reality, because they are trying to establish what people should consider to be normal conditions.

But in order to understand that it is possible to bring about a great positive effect in this direction (I do believe that if general public interest in this matter were to arise through following the ideas and methods indicated by anthroposophic science, then those people who searched for the spiritual element in the proper sense would come upon these insights by themselves), much more is necessary than what is being done now, when people are advised in this way: "You should pray, because by praying this or that will happen." You'll be able to gain insight and reach a conclusion only by applying the powers of mind, intellect, soul, heart, spirit, and imagination. This is what "looking at something spiritually" really means. Yes, gentlemen, these things can be properly ascertained only in this way; modern science is not acquainted with such an all-encompassing viewpoint. These are simple matters that you can gain knowledge about, as, for instance, at which particular time (let's say at the time of a couple's engagement) honey can be most useful.

As I've just indicated, it is truly something to marvel at how the bee sucks the honey nectar commonly available in nature, transforms it within itself, and produces honey, which is so extraordinarily useful for human life. You'll begin to understand how honey originates if I tell you about the same process in a completely different form, as it is found in the neighbors or relatives of the bees: the wasps. However, from wasps you can't get anything similar to honey that would be beneficial to mankind, although medicine has found a way to make great use of another product that wasps produce. But the way wasps work is quite different from that of bees. Next time, I'll also tell you about ants. But let's first examine a specific type of wasp—*Cynipidae.*

There are wasps that have the unusual trait of laying their eggs just about anywhere—in plants, in trees, and, for example, in leaves or the bark of trees. There are even some that lay them in the blossoms of trees. It would look like this

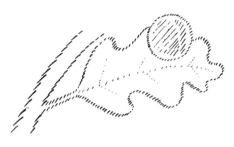

[table VIII, page 165, upper middle]. There is a branch and there, let's say, an oak leaf. The wasp, using its ovipositor (a stinger that is hollow inside) deposits its egg on the oak leaf. What happens now? The entire leaf tissue surrounding the spot where the wasp egg was placed undergoes a complete transformation. The leaf would have grown very differently if the egg had not been placed there. Let's now look at what arises at this spot. Here the growth of the plant has been changed completely, and around the wasp egg, sticking out of the leaf, a gall is formed. These galls are brownish in appearance. But how do they arise? They arise from the changed plant substance that now surrounds the wasp egg. Normally this wasp egg would not thrive if it were placed just anywhere. It can thrive only if this protective substance, which the wasp steals from the plant, is present.

The bee places its egg into the comb, and the egg becomes a larva, the larva a pupa, and, finally, the pupa a bee, which goes out to steal a plant substance and convert it within itself to something else. The wasp also does this, but somewhat earlier than the bee. The wasp, by placing the egg into the plant, takes the substance it needs from the plant at that time. The bee, however, waits somewhat longer than the wasp before it begins using the plant substance. With higher animals and humans, the egg already has a protective covering in the mother's body. That which the mother herself produces to protect the egg, the wasp needs to take from the plant in this instance. The gall is produced by the plant around the egg in the same way that in humans the placenta, which is expelled at birth, protects the growing embryo and fetus within the mother.

You notice how the wasp comes together with the plant. In areas where many such wasps live, you will observe that the trees are covered completely with such galls. This type of wasp and this type of tree have a symbiotic relationship. The wasp is 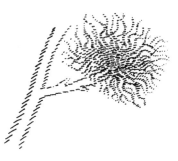 dependent on the tree and would not be able to procreate without having the plant create the protective shell around the egg. These galls can take on different appearances. Some don't look like apples, but rather like hair that has become entangled.[3] But everywhere you will find in the center the wasp egg. Sometimes these galls take the form of small shaggy nuts [table VIII, right]. This demonstrates how wasps live together with plants. Then, when the wasp has matured sufficiently, it drills its way out using its mandibles, to live as an adult until it, repeating the cycle, places its egg into another leaf. The placement of eggs always involves a symbiotic relationship with plants.

Now you could perhaps ask, "What does this have to do with the preparation of honey?" Gentlemen, it has a lot to do with it, and you can learn how honey is created if you consider this matter. Once again you'll find that in folk wisdom,

---

3. These are the rose galls of the rose gall wasp, *Rhodites rosae.*

in the instinctive agricultural knowledge that has been passed down generation by generation, just such a thing is taken into account. You perhaps know that in the southern regions—Greece, to be specific—figs play an important role.[4] There are the so-called wild figs, which are somewhat sweet but not sweet enough for some people with a sweet tooth. So what do these people do to bring about even sweeter figs? Imagine that this represents a wild fig tree. This wild fig tree is very attractive to a particular type of wasp, which places its eggs into the fig. Imagine that this is the wild fig tree with a fig growing on the branch, and that this fig contains the egg the wasp has laid [table VIII, left].

The fig grower is really a rather smart person. The grower allows the wasps to lay their eggs in the wild fig trees. Afterward, two such figs are taken down at a particular point in time when the wasp larvae have not finished developing and still have a long way to go before they would normally emerge. In any case, they have

---

4. From *Brehm's Illustrated Animal Life*, p. 511, op. cit.: "It is well-known that the people of antiquity knew how to make use of the gall wasp (*Cynips Psenes Linn's*, or today *Blastophaga psenes*) so as to obtain juicier and better-tasting figs. Even today the Greeks take great pains to use this animal properly to achieve caprification (*Caprificus* means "wild fig"), which improves the flavor of wild figs that have been enhanced in this way. This animal lives in the wild figs and achieves maturity at the end of June, when the figs are still unripe. These animals would stay in the figs were it not for the fact that people disturb them by picking them, tying them together with a long stalk of rush, throwing them in this form back onto a wild fig tree, all the while trying to distribute them equally on the tree. The process of drying out and shrinking of these wild figs causes these insects to crawl out, leave their home, and seek out other figs as their new home for a new brood, a second, abnormal generation. Before this second brood can achieve maturity, the figs are harvested for their enhanced properties of more juice and sweetness, a quality caused by the presence of the doomed insect."

finished a portion of their development. What happens now? The fig grower takes a stalk of rush and ties together these two figs containing the undeveloped wasp larvae in such a way that they'll hold together. Now this person goes to another fig tree, which has figs that need to be improved, and hangs on that tree the figs tied together because they contain the eggs that the wasp deposited there [table VIII, middle]. What happens now?

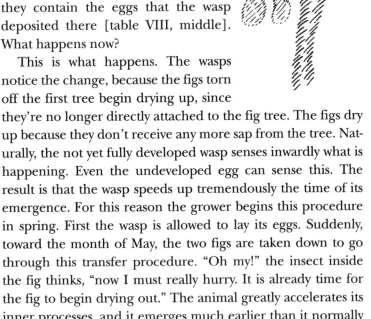

This is what happens. The wasps notice the change, because the figs torn off the first tree begin drying up, since they're no longer directly attached to the fig tree. The figs dry up because they don't receive any more sap from the tree. Naturally, the not yet fully developed wasp senses inwardly what is happening. Even the undeveloped egg can sense this. The result is that the wasp speeds up tremendously the time of its emergence. For this reason the grower begins this procedure in spring. First the wasp is allowed to lay its eggs. Suddenly, toward the month of May, the two figs are taken down to go through this transfer procedure. "Oh my!" the insect inside the fig thinks, "now I must really hurry. It is already time for the fig to begin drying out." The animal greatly accelerates its inner processes, and it emerges much earlier than it normally would. Had the fig remained attached to the tree, the wasp would have come out at the end of the summer. But now it has to emerge in early summer, and as a result of coming out this early it is forced into creating a second brood. It lays a second set of eggs during the summer, while it normally would have waited until the following spring to do so.

To lay this second set of eggs, the wasp goes over to the other figs growing on the same tree, the ones that the grower hopes to improve. It places its eggs into them, eggs that don't achieve maturity and develop only to a certain degree. What happens as a result? The figs containing the second brood become twice as sweet as the other wild figs. This is what is called the enrichment or improvement of figs, because they become twice as sweet.

What has happened here? The wasps, although related to bees, are in comparison very different because, in the form of an egg, they have already taken from the plant what potentially can become honey. If you, in such a clever fashion as the fig grower, were to tie together, using a stalk of rush, two of your wild figs containing wasp eggs and swing them up into the tree so that they hang up there, and if in this way you caused them to once again weave into the plant what they have absorbed from another plant, then you would be able to cause the wasp to inject this honey as a form of added sweetness into these now improved figs. The wasp injects this extra sweetness into the improved figs by thinly distributing the honey within them. This happens in a roundabout way that nature provides.

You can see that we have not taken anything out of nature but rather have allowed the true nature of honey to remain what it really is. A wasp is unable to prepare honey the same way that a bee does; the organization of this insect isn't even suited for that. But if you force the wasp to take this detour, it can transfer, during its reproductive cycle, to one plant the sweetness of the honey it has extracted from another plant. It thus makes this second, improved fig sweet, and you'll find in it a kind of honey-like substance. With this example we have come upon something very noteworthy. It becomes evident that these wasps have a body incapable of extracting from nature a nectar-like substance and converting it within themselves into honey. But using natural processes, they can make possible a certain type of honey creation involving the transfer of something from one fig to another.

The bee is a creature that has developed its wasp-like body to such an extent that it can carry on independently, away from the tree, the process that the wasp can carry on only in the tree itself. We need to realize that the bee is an insect that maintains within itself the power that the wasp has only as long as it is very young, that is, in the egg, larva, or pupa stage. The wasp loses the power to produce honey after it matures, but the bee maintains it even as an adult. Just consider, gentlemen, what it means when a person can look out into all of nature and say that in plants you can find honey, this substance that tends toward being a sugary sweet substance. It's just simply in there somehow. But you can make it appear, if only you follow the right paths. And you can do so by lending support to already existing natural processes, such as causing the wasp to move at the proper time to another tree, the fruits of which you wish to make sweeter.

Up here in our area you can't do things such as this anymore; especially now, in our present day and age, these things are no longer possible to achieve. But there once was a time in the development of the Earth when there was the possibility of taking wasps, as we still do today and others did even two thousand years ago, and using them in such a way as the clever wild fig grower does. By forcing a second brood in the same year and allowing them to emerge prematurely, the possibility existed for allowing wasps to emerge and to deposit their eggs into the mature figs that had already been picked; by doing this little by little for a long time, growers once succeeded in breeding wasps into bees. A bee is an animal that was bred from wasps a very long time ago. Today you can still see in animal activity, in the activity of wasps specifically, how the preparation or creation of honey existed in nature itself before the existence of bees.

And from this example you can also determine what the facts may be about bees putting their honey into combs in a very definite manner. The comb consists mainly of a wax substance. Note also that this wax substance isn't necessary just as a place for the honey to be deposited. It is necessary for the bee to secrete the wax. But it's also the case that a bee can prepare honey only if its whole body is functioning properly.

The second fig tree, in which the sweetness arises by itself, also has a richer wax content than the original wild fig tree. This increased wax content is one of the most important differences between the improved fig tree and the wild one. Nature, all by itself, creates this additional wax. It is this improved, sweetened fig, growing and thriving on a tree, that makes itself, to a certain degree, waxier than it was before. Here you can find the primitive prototype that prefigures what is later found in bee culture.

If you want to examine these facts in greater detail, you can take a cut through a stem from the improved tree, and what you'll find, strangely enough, when you look carefully, are markings that look like wax cells [table VIII, lower right]. Out

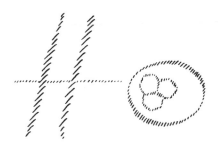

of the wax that accumulates inside the stem, growths such as these, specifically a type of bee cell, begin to form. The improved fig becomes richer in wax content, and inside the stem the wax organizes itself into something resembling a cell form. You may come to the following conclusion. If we examine this process for improving figs, what we have is a natural, but primitive method for producing honey, the only difference being that the honey remains within the fig.

The bee places, if I may express it this way, before the public eye that which remains hidden within nature in the case of the improved fig. With the help of the wasp, nature is able to do the same in this way. The wax is pushed up into the fig, the wax that would otherwise have remained in the stem and created cells through natural formation, cells that are not massive or very obvious but are simply hinted at and disappear again quickly. In this way the entire wax and honey formation is located in the fig. This entire bee culture is located within the tree, so that we can truly say that nature generally is a beekeeper.

What does a bee do first? A bee lays an egg into the comb, and the egg matures. Now it doesn't need to transform a substance into a gall nut but simply takes the nectar directly from the plant. It doesn't have to go to another tree that has a greater wax content but instead creates from itself that which otherwise is formed in the stem, the comb structure, and puts juice into it, now known as honey, whereas this juice is distributed throughout the entire fig in the case of the improved fig. You could also say that with bees, a process that nature normally restricts to the realm of the tree alone is carried out openly, in public view, and then only with the cooperative effort of both the tree and the wasp. Now you should be able to see clearly what you have before you when you look at an artistically created honeycomb with its regularly constructed wax cells. It's really a marvelous thing to look at, isn't it, Mr. Müller? And to top it all, there is honey in the cells!

Yes, gentlemen, just look at this. Then you'll say that it is amazing that the bee seems to represent, in the construction of its wonderful comb cells made of wax, something that resembles an artistically constructed tree trunk with all its ramifications! The bee doesn't go into a tree to lay its eggs but instead builds for itself that which resembles a picture of a tree, and rather than first letting the figs grow on the tree, it places the honey into the honeycomb already prepared for it.

Thus we have created with the bee, in this case, a copy of the process we saw in the artificially sweetened wild fig tree.

This has been an actual view into the innermost workings of nature. This example can show you what it is that you can learn directly from nature. You simply have to become acquainted with what is really out there in nature. Human beings still have much to learn about nature, but first they must find and see in operation the spirit element at work. Only then will they learn such things. Otherwise you will, like all the rest, stand there gaping when you travel south and observe the clever person who ties together reed stalks that have holes pricked into them and swings them up into a wild fig tree. You will stand there open-mouthed like the other travelers, even some scientists among them, who do not know why this person does such a thing. This person has pre-empted the work that bees normally do; the grower does this by allowing nature to put honey into the figs. And these figs, in the region where they thrive, are in a similar way as healthy as honey, because a primitive form of honey is present in them, as provided directly by nature without the help of bees.

These are things you should call to mind when you wish to discuss anything as important and as penetrating to the mind as beekeeping. I believe that, with this information, you will gradually be able to move toward acquiring a somewhat more correct way of looking at these matters.

Question and Answer Period

R. Hahn: After the lecture, I approached Dr. Steiner and asked, "What is the cause of a foul brood?"[5] He commented that he would be able to say something definite about this

---

5. "Foul brood" refers to a destructive disease of honeybee larvae caused by a bacteria.

only after he had really done some research regarding this disease. But probably a queen bee's foul brood had something to do with its defective composition of uric acid. He then said, "It's true, isn't it, that a bee also has uric acid in its system, so the probable cause of this disease is the imperfect compounding of uric acid."

Regarding the breeding of wasps into bees, as mentioned in the same lecture, he responded approximately as follows to a related query: "This process took place during the Atlantean age on the old continent of Atlantis, at a time when the individual animal forms were not yet as fixed as they are today, and when the boundaries between the various families and genera were not yet as rigidly established as they are now. Today such a far-ranging crossbreeding would not be possible anymore."

· Lecture Six

Dornach, December 12, 1923

*Someone asks a question about the relationship between bees and
flowers. He wants to know what kind of relationship it is that ties
them together and what importance honey has for human beings.
Once again a reference is made to the deposition of eggs.*

Dr. Steiner: Well, gentlemen, we want to talk about that once
again in today's lecture. This is what it's all about. We have
this fertilization of the queen during her fertilization flight.
The queen then has been fertilized. At that point we have to
consider the time span between the egg-laying and when the
insect is completely mature as a bee. For a queen, the time
span is sixteen days, for a worker twenty-one days, and for a
drone twenty-two to twenty-four days. These three types of
bees are different from one another with regard to the time
when they reach maturity. What is the basis of all this? In
order that a larva become a queen, the bees feed it in a special way. The queens are fed somewhat differently to accelerate their growth.

As it turns out, the bee is a creature more directly influenced by the Sun than other animals; it is a "Sun" creature.
The Sun needs about as much time to rotate on its axis as a
drone needs to mature. The queen, in its development
toward maturity, does not wait for even one complete rotation of the Sun, which means that it stays completely within
the realm of a single rotation. By doing so, the queen places

itself entirely under the influence of the Sun, which then allows it to become an egg-producing bee. Everything that is connected with the capability to lay eggs is under the influence of the Sun, also in respect to the entire cosmos.

At the moment when a type of feeding takes place that causes the bee's development to be accelerated to such an extent that it almost passes through one complete rotation of the Sun, the way the workers do, the bee comes closer to falling under the influence of the Earth and its development. The more the Sun continues in its rotation, the more the bee comes under the influence of Earth development. To be sure, the worker is still very much a Sun creature, but it is also a bit of an "Earth" creature. And the drone, which develops through the course of a complete rotation of the Sun, is completely an Earth creature; it has freed itself of the Sun's influence. Now we have three sorts of bees—the Sun queen; the worker, which still has some extra-earthly powers; and the drone, which has nothing at all of the Sun's effects and is completely an Earth creature. Everything that normally takes place does not happen under the influence of the Earth's powers; only fertilization does.

The strange thing is this. Just observe the fertilization flight. The lower animals do not enjoy fertilization; they really want to escape from it if possible. We can prove that everywhere with many examples. For this reason it is really a flight that the queen undertakes in the direction of the Sun. For fertilization does not take place when the skies are overcast. When the flight occurs, the drones that want to take the earthly element and fuse it with the Sun element have to battle it out in the air. Those that are weak remain behind. Only those that have a sufficient reserve of power and can fly as high as the queen are capable of bringing about fertilization.

Just because the queen has been fertilized doesn't mean that every egg has been fertilized. Actually, gentlemen, only a portion of the queen's eggs are fertilized. Those are the ones that will become workers or queens. The unfertilized eggs in the queen's body will become drones. When a queen has not been fertilized at all, only drones will come from her eggs. When the queen is fertilized, drones develop from the unfertilized eggs, or workers and queens from the fertilized ones. When the embryos have been fertilized, it means that the heavenly element in the embryo has been touched by the earthly element. Even then, when there are drones along with workers, the drones owe their existence to the fact that they have been exposed most of all to the earthly element, because fertilization hasn't occurred. And these drones must then be further exposed to the earthly element, so that they can remain viable. They have to pass through a longer period of being fed than do the other bees, and so on. Are you satisfied with this explanation?

Questioner: Years ago I once heard that a person's rheumatism abates when he or she is stung by a bee or wasp.

Dr. Steiner: On this point I can return to something that I perhaps did not cover last Monday. Mr. Müller talked about a man who, it appears, had heart problems and collapsed after being stung by a bee.

Mr. Müller: The doctor advised him to give up beekeeping because it could lead to his death!

Dr. Steiner: Heart disease can signify nothing other than that, in the case of this man, the I-organization is not properly directing, controlling, or engaging the body as it normally does. To understand this situation, you have to reflect back to something else I've mentioned in my lectures. You know that we have to differentiate four parts that make up a human being [table IX, page 165]: the physical body that you can touch; the etheric body; the astral body; and the I, or I-being. This I exerts its control in the blood; it actually moves the blood. And as the blood is being driven by the I, the heart responds and beats. Everywhere in books, you will find the incorrect presentation of facts regarding the heart. The books will explain how the heart is simply a pump and that from there the blood is pumped throughout the entire body. This is nonsense, because in reality the blood is not pumped but rather driven forward by the I itself, and as a result it comes into motion everywhere.

If someone maintains that the heart drives the blood to where it needs to go in the body, that person should likewise maintain that if a turbine were to be set up somewhere, then, according to this logic, the turbine drives the water. But everybody knows that the water drives the turbine. Likewise a human being has such places of resistance within. The blood hits this resistance and drives the heart. The only difference is that the blood comes up against this resistance only once, and while the oxygen and carbon dioxide are combining, it pushes backward. In so doing, the blood snaps forward once and then backward once. This is how the heartbeat arises. In this way it comes about that the I activates the blood circulation in human beings.

Now it is true that the I is also present in a very mysterious way in bee poison. That, gentlemen, which you have as an I-force circulating in your blood is also present in bee poison. It is interesting that a bee needs this poison in its body. The bee doesn't need bee poison only for the purpose of stinging. It is merely coincidental that a bee is able to sting. A bee needs this bee poison in its body because it requires the same power to circulate fluids as a human being does to circulate blood.

A beehive, I've told you before, can be likened to a complete human being. Consider for a moment that bee poison gets into your body somehow, that is, into your bloodstream. Imagine also that you are a normal, healthy human being. Your blood, energized by the bee poison, is set into greater motion than under normal circumstances. This will cause some irritation and possibly inflammation somewhere, but your heart will be able to withstand it. If, however, the heart is diseased, then the I is strengthened and increased dangerously by the effect of the additional bee poison entering the bloodstream. This poison will push hard against a somewhat diseased heart valve, the result being that a person may become unconscious or even die. This is the case Mr. Müller was talking about.

The strange thing, however, is that anything and everything that can make a person sick or even kill a person can also have curative powers that bring about healing. And whoever prepares medicines or remedies has a grave responsibility, because there are no correct medications that, if they are used incorrectly, would not bring about the very illness that such a person was trying to cure by using them. If you are able to bring about a certain degree of unconsciousness or even death in giving someone bee poison, what is really happening? Well, you see, when a person becomes unconscious, the astral body and, specifically, the I pull themselves out of the physical body, the way they normally do in a healthy manner during sleep; but during unconsciousness it happens in an abnormal manner. During unconsciousness, the I becomes stuck instead of leaving the body entirely, as it does during sleep. If a person has a weak I, that individual is unable to enter back into the physical body. You need to shake this person well, so that the individual can wake up out of unconsciousness. You may need to increase the breathing and undertake other similar activities. You may have to apply certain manual maneuvers. You probably know about this, too—in such cases you need to take a person's forearms, cross them above the chest, put them back again, and then repeat this procedure. This is done to make the unconscious person breathe artificially. These artificial methods for stimulating breathing have one main goal—to bring the I back into the physical body properly.

Assume the following circumstance, for example: someone has rheumatism or even gout or other deposits in the body. In this case, you will need to strengthen the I. For what reason does a person get rheumatism or gout? Because the I-organization is too weak. It is unable to influence the blood to move properly. It needs a special stimulus. If the blood does not have the correct amount of movement—for example, it may flow too slowly in a person's system—then tiny crystals may settle out all over, and these crystals will move into the area around the arteries. These tiny crystals consist of uric acid. They begin filling the entire body. This condition is gout or rheumatism, and it arises when the I–organization is too weak.

If I give such a person the proper dose of bee or wasp poison, the I will be strengthened. But it is very important not to give too much, otherwise the I will not be able to take over control. If you give just the right amount, so that the I-organization is strengthened, then you can make a very good medicine from bee or wasp poison. But it is important to mix it with other medicines. Such things are done. For example, the old *Tartarus* remedy was made in a similar way; however, it contained other substances.

You can always create medications with these poisons, as in this instance to strengthen the I. But if you want to apply such a medication, you really need to know the patient in question. Say, for example, someone has gout or rheumatism. The first question to ask is whether the heart is healthy, that is, does it function well when the circulation of blood works upon it? If this is so, then you can heal such a person with bee or wasp

poison. If the heart is not healthy, you'll need to make a deci-
sion between alternatives. If the individual has heart disease
caused by a nervous condition, the negative effects of adminis-
tering bee or wasp poison will not be very great, but if the diseased heart condition is due to a defective heart valve, you'll
need to be very careful about using this type of medication.
The blood will push very hard upon the valve and the heart in
general. On no account should this type of medicine be given
if the heart valve is diseased. This is the way things are. This is
why it is so dangerous to say generally that a specific medicine
should be used for this or that illness. You could easily prepare
a medication with wasp or bee poison in it (we have such
homeopathic medicines) and mix it with some other binding
agent, with gelatinous or other binding agents derived from
plants, and then put it into an ampule and inject it, the same
way a bee sting injects poison. Only, in this case, the reaction
you get from a bee is a much stronger one. You can manufacture this medicine and say, "This is a remedy for rheumatism."

Yes, gentlemen, this isn't the only thing you need to be
concerned about. You need to consider whether the patient
can tolerate the medication based upon the general organic
condition of the person's health. Such medicines, which can
affect deeper levels of the human organism, ought not to be
given unless you have examined the patient's general condition of health. There is no way around it; you must evaluate
and become thoroughly acquainted with the patient's state of
health. If somewhere you find remedies that are generally
accepted and said to be good for this or that kind of illness,
then these are usually remedies that do not cause much harm
and will nevertheless have some beneficial effect. Such medicines can become commercially available. You can even
accept the fact that, in reality, there may be some unpleasant
results for the patient. The process of curing always has some
unpleasant results accompanying it. The patient will always

have to overcome the bad side-effects of the treatment, whenever you try to cure the individual of any disease.

Today there are people who undergo a course of treatment when they aren't really sick. Before the war there were many more cases like this. The doctors in countries with a weak currency are suffering the most now, because people aren't taking these cures as much as before. It used to be that the entire range of patients, from healthy to extremely ill, would participate in such cures; now only the most gravely ill do so! If you have a very strong person who begins to suffer from rheumatism—usually it is not really rheumatism, but rather a gout-like condition—then a bee sting, just as Mr. Burle indicated, would have an extraordinarily beneficial effect. Such an individual can be healed because this person can tolerate the sting without any serious problems.

It usually happens that a normal person with rheumatism, if given a proper dose of bee poison that has been specially prepared for this individual, naturally can tolerate it as a remedy and can even be cured with it. But the poison from a bee sting itself will cause such a strong inflammation that this inflammation will first need to be healed, and, in order to do so, the bee poison needs to be removed as fast as possible by the body, the result being that not much of the bee poison will be left in the body to cure the rheumatism. With most normally healthy human beings, this will likely be the case—that there won't be much poison left over to treat the patient. But now let's take the following case. Rheumatism can also occur in another way. A person does not work much physically but eats a lot. Such a person will usually have a rather healthy heart until, in the process of not working much but eating a lot, the whole matter begins to be fraught with problems.

The heart is an extraordinarily resistant organ and will allow itself to be corrupted from within only after very many years unless hereditary factors or serious problems during childhood indicate otherwise. But a person who eats very large quantities of food often drinks alcoholic beverages along with the meal. By doing this, the I is stimulated, and the circulation of blood becomes very intense. Then the beating heart no longer has enough strength to accommodate this increased activity. Various poisons—uric acid and others—are deposited everywhere. The circumstances might have it that the heart remains quite strong for a long while in the body where gout and rheumatism are already present. Under circumstances such as these, a bee sting can provide true benefit for such a person with this type of condition.

Mr. Burle: I don't know if an alcoholic condition existed in the case of the man we're talking about.

Dr. Steiner: You mean, you didn't investigate this possibility? You see, that's the very thing you must clarify in a situation like this where you want to use a remedy like bee poison—and that is a strong remedy. You must pay extremely close attention to everything about this person's condition of health.

Mr. Müller stated that he had gotten rheumatism due to a cold and had treated it through exposure to the Sun. It went away after that but had returned somewhat during the summer. He also had believed that bee stings could be beneficial; but once he'd had a very unfortunate day when he received approximately thirty-two bee stings on both legs. The only negative effect he was aware of was that, for eight days, he saw nothing but rainbow colors all over his legs. A bee sting does not always cause a swelling. The human body varies a great deal in this regard. As indicated, someone can die from a single bee sting, and another can have as many as sixty bee stings at one time without making the heart beat any faster. One person simply has a greater resistance to bee stings than another.

Dr. Steiner. When you received all those bee stings at one time, had you already been working with bees for a long time?

Mr. Müller: Many years!

Dr. Steiner: You probably cannot recall your first bee sting. The first time someone is stung, the person will usually feel the effect to some degree. The man you told us about was most likely stung by a bee for the first time. Once you've had such a poison in your body, in your blood, your ability to cope with this poison will increase; you'll be immunized more and more, as they say. If someone has been stung a bit at the outset of involvement with beekeeping, and if such a person is otherwise in good health, then this sting will have the effect of making the individual less and less sensitive to stings. If you know you're healthy, you can even go so far as to allow yourself to be stung several times. The usual symptoms will occur, the appearance of rainbow colors and so forth, but the whole process is more of an external thing. The blood has been immunized. That doesn't depend only on the I but also on what has been put into the blood beforehand. I'm astonished that the doctor who observed this case that you've told us about didn't tell the man that the second time the effect would not be so bad and the third time he'd be immunized. But perhaps he had such a severe heart condition that he couldn't be exposed to this danger. This is something that must also be taken into account.

It's also true, isn't it, that this becomes a dangerous situation only because there are doctors who think that every beekeeper should be immunized before beginning to work with bees. When people go into the armed services, their bodies are saturated with all kinds of shots given to them before they go onto the battlefield. That's also something that is not to be recommended. That shouldn't be done, because the blood can become a place for the creation of garbage. A person's blood always suffers deterioration when these things are put into the system. After some time the blood reaches its former equilibrium again. At that time the blood is healthy, to be sure, but it is protected against new poisons of the same type.

Mr. Müller: With regard to the drones and the three types of eggs, Dr. Steiner, you've covered everything so far, but there is one point you may not be aware of. If the beehive, in my opinion, is very healthy, there still will be times when the queen is of an inferior quality or when the queen is too old, and the entire brood created by the queen turns into drones. After thirty years of experience in beekeeping, I am convinced that such an inferior queen, despite her illness or the weakness of old age, is still capable of laying an occasional good egg, although the majority of the eggs will become drones.

Then I would like to know about the matter of the honey production of bees—how they create it and if the beekeeper should assist the process with sugar. From your discussion of this matter, it appears as if the beekeeper shouldn't use any sugar. If someone feeds the bees sugar during the time when they are creating honey, that person is blacklisted—just like when you don't want a worker anymore after the worker has done something to displease you as an employer.

Dr. Steiner: You're right about the fact that you won't get the same product if you apply sugar artificially. And if someone wanted to enjoy an extra quantity of sugar along with the honey, then that can be added by the individual. It would be wrong to put water into someone's wine because your personal goal is that people shouldn't drink such strong wine. In this case it is more important that a person receive exactly what is printed on the label of the bottle. It has to be this way.

Regarding this matter, I would say that the mutual supervision by beekeepers of their products is the best way to go, because they are the ones who understand beekeeping best of all.

I'd still like to say this about the matter concerning the drones. It could happen that you might immediately suspect that the queen hasn't been fertilized properly, and, as a result, too many drones hatch. In this case, you could, if you didn't want to let the bees do this themselves (if too many drones hatch, the bees won't do it; experiments like this have been conducted), by feeding them yourself quite vigorously and getting them to hatch earlier, not in twenty-three or twenty-four days but rather in twenty to twenty-two days. This way you can at least make them into workers, into being similar to workers, but a slower, straggling type of worker. This is never a long-term solution, but you can see from this what an important role time plays in this matter.

Naturally, these are things that are never carried out in the practical world of beekeeping; but theoretically they exist. You could say that the effect of what you feed them is truly very strong, and you can't dispute the fact that in certain isolated cases, it is possible to turn a worker into a bee that could lay a few eggs, but a true queen it is not. All of this goes to show you how mutable such an animal is. But this doesn't have much of an influence on the practical aspects of beekeeping.

Mr. Müller: That's what we call a pseudo queen, which is due to a diseased beehive.

Dr. Steiner: There is no great importance in this for the practical aspects of beekeeping. In the beehive there simply is this tendency for bees to be able to change a would-be worker into an egg-laying queen by applying a special method of feeding it. This is a type of illness. The beehive is a single entity. In this case the entire beehive is sick. It would be just like force-feeding a goose to fatten it. It is at this point that the powers of the liver are developed to an abnormal degree. The liver becomes overly healthy, and the entire organism becomes sick. If you make a worker into a queen, then this queen is, in reality, an overly healthy worker, but the entire beehive should be considered ill. Perhaps you will think of something else to ask in the future. We can always revisit this subject. Today I would still like to say a few words that will be connected with Mr. Dollinger's question.

We can distinguish clearly between the insects that are bee-like, in an extended sense of the term: bees, wasps, and ants. These animals are related to one another. Last time I told you about the interesting story concerning the gall wasp that places its eggs in trees and similar plants, and I pointed out and showed you that these wasps cause a special type of honey preparation to take place within the tree or plant. But there are also other types of wasps. These are more similar to bees in that they construct combs.

There is, for example, an interesting type of wasp that builds as follows. If there is a rather stiff leaf on a branch, this wasp will fetch, from a place it flies to somewhere nearby, very tiny pieces that it can bite from the bark or similar substances. Then it saturates them with its saliva and begins making a few stalks from this substance. After it has made these stalks, the wasp continues this process and begins adding to these stalks something that looks like the single cell wall of a honeycomb. But if you examine the substance, you will find that it is different. The honeycomb consists of what you all know to be wax. But when you take this substance from the wasp, it is grayish and appears to be very similar to what we know as paper. It is really a kind of paper substance. Then the wasp adds a second, third, and fourth cell to it and these cells

hang up there in the tree. They cover the cells after the eggs have been placed into them. And now, while the egg-laying is taking place, the wasp uses its paper to create a ribbon [table IX] and then a kind of lid. It leaves the nest open on one side: that's an entry hole through which it can fly back and forth and service these cells.

Then it adds more cells and repeats the entire process once again. This can become a very long cone, just like a fir cone. So the wasp builds for itself a structure like a fir cone, the individual parts of which consist of a paper-like material but with a cell structure resembling a honeycomb. Other wasps' nests are, as you know, covered by a skin. Wasps' nests have all sorts of shapes. Consider for a moment what is really happening here. If you ask me what a bee does in order to make its cells out of wax, I have to tell you that the bee flies to flowers or to that which is similar on trees; a bee is much less interested in the bark or other parts of the wood. For the most part the bee goes to the blossom or perhaps even to that part of the blossom that is already partially leaflike, but this, of course, much less often than the blossom.

There is one instance where higher insects, such as bees, seek out something other than blossoms—they don't go to the various parts of wood or similar substances, but they may go to something else that is very attractive to their sense of taste. The bees do less of this, but more specifically wasps and, even more so, ants do it. Although they use, on the one hand, harder substances, such as the wooden parts of a tree, for construction (contrary to bees), ants and wasps also enjoy, on the other hand, the juice that comes from the aphids that live on plants. This is very interesting. The harder the material is that these animals use for their construction, the more they will love not only blossom juice but also that which resembles the blossom most of all—the aphids. These are very precious animals—excuse me for expressing this more in terms of what an ant would say. The aphids are completely a plant blossom. The juice they secrete is, for the ants, the finest possible honey that anyone could want. In the case of wasps, you will notice, for example, that they have become connoisseurs in this regard.

When we examine ants, we'll notice that they don't have the power to create such a nest as the wasp builds. Ants do this differently. They pile up the soil, and in this soil you'll find passageways everywhere, a complete maze of passageways. And this maze continues underground. Using these passageways, the ants drag into the nest things that they can use—the harder substances of plants and of trees. Ants love specifically that portion of the wood that is already dead. They seek out what they need in order to continue constructing their nest, which is made of many little pieces of earth. They like to go to a wood stump left after a tree has been cut down. Here they find very hard inner wood as well as bark, which they then drag back to their nest and use as construction material.

[Text on blackboard, table IX, upper left:
Bee: Juice of Flowers: Wax Cells
Wasp: Juice of Flowers, Juice of Animals: Harder Cells
Ant: Juice of Animals: No Cells]

So it is that ants use the hardest material of all for the construction of their nest. They are unable to make this material

into a cell that might be part of a comb structure. This is
beyond their capability. They use material that is too hard. So
you can see that bees use the material that is present in the
flowers. They make the comb structure from it, but this forces
them also to derive their nourishment from the juice of the
blossom. With wasps we find that they use a somewhat harder
material resembling paper to build their cell structures. This
is a harder material, but it is thin and, naturally, more brittle
than a honeycomb; in itself it is nevertheless harder.

A wasp resembles a gourmet when it comes to aphids, but
it still derives some nourishment from that which is in plants,
the same way bees do. Ants, however—which use such a hard
material or substance that all they can do with it is construct
passageways or tiny caverns in the soil, but not combs or cell
structures—really love aphids. You will even find that some
ants take the aphids into their nest, where they can "milk"
them [table IX, lower right].

All over the ant heap, you'll find small structures where
the aphids are located. For ants, these are their "cows." What
the ants do is on a correspondingly lower level. They have a
barn filled not with cows but with aphids. The ants go up to
the aphids and stroke them with their antennae. The aphid
enjoys this feeling and secretes some of its juice. As a result,
the ant is able to suck up the juice obtained by stroking the
aphid. The most important part of what an ant needs as food
is derived in this manner from the aphid. With cows it is
somewhat similar, the only difference being that the stroking

must be much more vigorous. You could say that ants really milk their aphids. They capture them on flowers and leaves where the aphids are found, and they take very good care of them. You could say that it's really wonderful that there are aphids. And, specifically, it is wonderful for the ants when there are aphids nearby. Then the aphids are carefully collected by the ants and put into a "barn," where they are used. What an ingenious arrangement of nature that these small animals can be engaged in a commercial dairy business involving aphids!

The ant, which needs such hard materials for its own structure, is not able to be satisfied simply with the juice of plants. It needs as food that which the flower juice has given to an animal. This juice of a flower must have first passed through an animal. You might say that bees need pure flower juice and wasps need flower juice and animal juice and, in return for that, make harder cells. With the ant, nourishment is derived only from animal juice, and that's why there are no actual cells. The ant does not have the power to create cells; it must have the additional food it gets from its little animal shed, even though it is still capable of obtaining something from flowers. Otherwise the ant can't live.

You see what an interesting relationship there is between the flowers and these animals. The bees need the flower juice in its pure form. The others, wasps and specifically ants, are forced to obtain this flower juice from other animals that have already digested it. But, in return, they are able to use for the construction of a shelter or a nest that which no longer is flower juice. There is truly a great difference between the bee's honeycomb made of wax, the wasp's nest made of paper, and the ant's structure, which can be created only externally and never completely becomes a cell. Nourishment is, in this case, the great distinguishing factor.

• Lecture Seven

Dornach, December 15, 1923

Good morning, gentlemen! Today I would like to continue the subject we were talking about, the one that followed from Mr. Dollinger's question last time. If other questions arise, we can try to take care of those too. Last time, in order to answer this question, I began discussing ants. We can say that they are related to bees, since they belong to the same order— bees, wasps, and ants. The only difference, as we observe them, is in their manner of living. From all of this we can actually learn a great deal that can be useful for managing things here on Earth. For the more you investigate these creatures and the manner in which they live, the more you will come to the conclusion that there is great wisdom in how they work and what they accomplish.

Last time I told you how ants build their nests and how they make their little mounds out of tiny fragments procured from the soil, from decaying or dead wood, and also from other construction materials that they put into this mix. Then they construct their earth mounds. In these mounds there are a variety of corridors through which they move in great numbers, in the form of processions. You can see them emerging from their holes and going different places to collect the things they want to collect.

Sometimes these creatures do not first build nests but rather use what is already there. Assume, for instance, that someone has cut down a tree. The stump of the tree that has been removed remains in the ground. Then an ant colony comes along, bores into the stump, and creates a chamber and also bores all the passageways that lead outside. They may even add soil to the structure as they build one passageway on top of another. These are all interconnected, thus creating a complete maze of corridors [table X, page 166]. Through these corridors the ants move and bring from the vicinity what they need for food and for the structure of the nest.

You see, gentlemen, it's all very fine simply to say that these ants do all these things instinctively—but in saying this, you really haven't said much. For if the ant doesn't have available to it such a tree stump, it proceeds to make a sand-hill type of nest. If it finds an appropriate tree stump, it saves itself the unnecessary work of constructing an earth-mound nest. The ant adjusts its work methods to suit the individual situations that exist. This makes it difficult to maintain the opinion that it has a general instinctive behavior. Such behavior would mean that it does everything according to its instincts. But the ant is able to adjust its activities according to the changing external circumstances. This is what is important.

This may not happen here very much, but as soon as you go to other regions lying farther south, ants can become a pest and cause considerable trouble. Imagine a house where, in an unfrequented corner, ants have taken up residence, have carried in all sorts of things from the vicinity—grains of soil, tiny pieces of wood—and have constructed a chamber unnoticed by the home owner, who hasn't cleaned the corner in a long time. Then they extend their passageways to the kitchen and the pantry, using very complicated routes, and they retrieve their food from those areas. Such a house in southern regions can become completely penetrated by one ant nest. You may not be aware that you are sharing your home with an ant colony, and you'll notice it only by chance, when you discover that something in the pantry has been nibbled at and you follow the trail back to its source.

Here, too, the word instinct doesn't explain much; otherwise you could say that nature has put instinct into these creatures to create their nest structure in that specific house. It would have to be made in just such a way that it would fit into the particular house. So you see, these creatures don't act according to pure instinct; there is instead a wisdom present in them. But if you examine a single ant all by itself, you would not come to the conclusion that it is particularly wise. That which the ant does under these conditions (or what you have it do), completely separated from its colony, does not have the appearance of any great wisdom. The result is that you have to consider the possibility that it's not the individual ant that has intelligence but rather the entire ant colony. Likewise, it is the entire beehive that is wise. The individual ants in the colony are not the ones that possess this intelligence. As a colony, however, the ants work in an extremely wise manner.

There is still much I would like to say about even more interesting things that happen. There is another type of ant that does the following. Somewhere on the ground it constructs a rather high mound; then it forms a circle surrounded by soil. There it burrows into the ground—in there are the ants. Sometimes this mound can turn out to look like a volcano. Inside are the passageways that radiate into the surrounding area. Well, these ants then engage in a very unusual action. They bite away and destroy all the grasses and plants that grow on the area they claim, with the exception of one type of grass.[1] Anything else they continually destroy. Sometimes they bite away and destroy everything, so that all that is left is the hill and around it an area that appears to be paved. This area appears paved because soil becomes more compact as all living plants are removed from it. It becomes very smooth and begins to look like asphalt pavement, only much lighter in color.

Now these ants go out farther into the surrounding area to find and bring back a specific grass, which they then plant. As soon as the wind blows other seeds into their cleared area and they begin to sprout, the ants very quickly bite off whatever appears above ground and carry it away from the nest and the area they have prepared. So it is that nothing can grow in this area except this single type of grass. The ants have laid claim to a parcel of land and have planted on it only what suits them. The grass that they grow has a very different appearance when you compare it with the same grass growing elsewhere. Usually this grass grows in a loose soil. That's why it has a different appearance. The soil that the ants have prepared is very hard, so that the grass that grows there produces extremely hard seeds, seeds as hard as a pebble [table X].

---

1. *Aristida stricta* and *Aristida oligantha. Aristida* means "needle grass"; both varieties are called "ant" rice.

Yes, gentlemen, you can find such ant colonies; these are agricultural ants (*Atta malefaciens*) that tend the fields around them! This is what Darwin, who has studied them carefully, calls them. You'll find the entire farm, the land as well as the extremely hard seeds. Then, when their crop is ready, the ants come out, bite off the portion above ground, and carry it back into the hill. For a while they remain in there, and you don't see them, but they are busy inside their anthill. Everything that they can't use, that might be attached to the seed, they bite off. After a while they come out again, go over and beyond their field to dump whatever they don't need, and keep the pebble-hard seeds, some of which they break open with their extremely hard jaws and eat and others of which they use to plant in their field. They are truly farmers. They look at things nearby to see if they can use them. Whatever they can't use, they throw out. After all, we don't do these things much differently. These agricultural ants work with great precision with those things that they need for themselves.

When you think about the way these endeavors are carried out, you may ask yourself what is really going on here. You see, a new type of grass is actually being created! These seeds that are like pebble-hard rice kernels don't exist anywhere else. They are created by these ants, which use them as part of a process that is repeated over and over again. What is really happening? Before we try to answer this question, let's look at this matter from another perspective. Let's go back to the wasps. There we'll find, as I have told you, creatures that lay their eggs in leaves or bark, out of which the so-called gall apples are formed, from which young wasps will eventually emerge.

This can also take place differently. There are caterpillars that look like this (draws on blackboard) [see table X, upper right]. All of you, I'm sure, are acquainted with this type of caterpillar, covered with thick, bristly hair. This is what can happen to such a caterpillar. One or more wasps of a certain type can come and lay their eggs directly into the caterpillar [ichneumon, or ichneumon fly]. When the eggs mature, the larvae emerge from these eggs. These larvae are the first form that the wasps take. Even bees and other insects of this type appear in this way. With ants it is also similar. You know, if you scratch away at an anthill long enough, you'll find the so-called ant eggs, which some people use as food for certain songbirds. However, these ant eggs are not really eggs but chrysalises. The eggs are small, and from these eggs the first thing to emerge are the larvae. It is incorrect to call these ant chrysalises "ant eggs."

What happens, when the wasp lays its eggs in the caterpillar, is a very remarkable matter. I've already told you about it once before.[2] The larvae that emerge from the eggs are voracious eaters. But now remember that there are countless larvae in this single caterpillar. With their voracious appetites, these larvae get their nourishment from the caterpillar's body. And here a very strange thing occurs. As soon as one of the wasp larvae begins eating the caterpillar's stomach, the entire mass of young wasps is doomed to a certain premature death; they are not able to continue living. If anything like an eye, a heart-like organ, or a similar organ were to serve as nourishment for the larvae or even be nibbled at, life for all concerned could not continue. These tiny wasp larvae demonstrate an understanding that directs them not to nibble at anything that the caterpillar needs for its continued existence; they eat only those organs that can be injured yet continue to exist for a long time in an impaired condition. The creature does not die; it will, at most, be sick. And so the wasp larvae can continue eating inside the caterpillar.

---

2. See "The Brain and Thinking," in *Health and Illness*, vol. 2, Anthroposophic Press, Spring Valley, NY, 1983 (GA 348).

This arrangement, that these wasp larvae simply will not bite into anything that could cause the caterpillar to die directly, has been established with great wisdom. Perhaps you have even seen this phenomenon, how the larvae emerge when they have matured sufficiently. They crawl out after the caterpillar has served with its entire body as a foster mother for the whole brood. They crawl out, develop into ichneumon flies, and seek out their nourishment from flowers and similar plants. And then, when they are mature enough, they will, in turn, place their eggs into similar caterpillars.

Now you could say that there is really something very intelligent in all of this! And, indeed, as I've told you, your astonishment will become greater the more you begin to observe these matters more carefully. You begin to marvel and then ask yourself what the connections are among all these things. Let's now get to the bottom of all of this. First we tell ourselves that there are the flowers that grow out of the ground. There are caterpillars present. Now these insects come and gorge themselves with what they find in the form of flowers and caterpillars; then they propagate themselves. This same story begins anew again and again. On the surface, it appears that this entire insect world could disappear and it would be no great loss for us as human beings. When we look at the bee, we say as human beings, "The bees produce honey for us, and, for this reason, beekeeping is useful to us." Fine. But that is looking at the whole matter only from the standpoint of human beings. If it turns out that bees can be considered robbers that simply take the honey away from the flowers, and we can then use this honey for nourishment or even curing diseases, the whole matter is considered to be very favorable from our viewpoint. But if you look at it from the viewpoint of the flowers, it would appear to be simply robbery, with human beings acting as accessories to the crime. You also must ask whether, from the standpoint of the flowers, you need to say, as they would, that out there are all these robbers—bees, wasps, ants—who take our juice away, and we would be able to grow and thrive much better if they didn't do this to us.

This is the standpoint that we assume the flowers would have. You can hear endless lamentations expressed by unknowledgeable people, who say, "O, these poor flowers and these poor creatures, the caterpillars! These terrible parasites attack and eat them up; they do all sorts of things to remove substances from the flowers." This is not, however, the way things really are, not at all. The situation is quite different from what you might think. If you come up close to a flower and you see an insect, let's say a bee, sitting on it and sucking up the juice contained in the flower or willow blossom, you must ask yourself what would happen to the plant if the bee, wasp, or other insect did not come to the plant and remove the juice from it. This is a more difficult question than the one concerning the simple act of robbery. You need to take a deep look into the entire ecology that nature has to offer. And here it is also true that you will not be able to form any meaningful opinion unless you can look back into the conditions that prevailed in much earlier periods of the Earth's development.

The Earth was not always the way we see it today. If the Earth had always been as it is now, with its dead limestone, dead quartz, dead gneiss, dead mica-schist; with its plants sprouting from present-day seeds; and with the animals and so on—if the Earth had always been this way, then the whole thing could not exist at all; nothing could exist at all! The people who take their knowledge only from what exists today have allowed themselves to be completely deceived, for this Earth could not exist all by itself. Gentlemen, that person who seeks the secrets of the Earth and wishes to know how things conform with the natural laws of Earth, but who uses the same sources and methods that contemporary science does, is like a visitor from Mars who would come to Earth and have no interest in living human beings but would prefer to go into a morgue and examine the corpses there. These corpses could not exist if they had not first been living human beings. You would first have to lead such a Martian, who had never before seen living human beings and was looking only at corpses, to living human beings and point them out to the Martian. Then the Martian would say, "Well, now I understand why the corpses have this particular form. Earlier I could not understand it because I was not yet acquainted with the living form that had preceded it." And so it is necessary to go back to earlier conditions if you want to understand the laws that govern the Earth's development. You see, a completely different form of the Earth preceded the one we have now. I've always called it the Moon-formation stage (see my *Outline of Esoteric Science*) because the present-day Moon is the leftover portion of the older Earth. Likewise, other conditions of the Earth preceded that one. The Earth has gone through transformations, and originally it took a very different form.

There once was on Earth a stage or condition where such plants and insects as we have them now did not exist at all. The situation was this. There was that which you might be able to compare to the present-day Earth. Growing out of it were, let's say, plantlike formations, but of a type that continually changed their shapes, in a manner similar to the way clouds do. Around the Earth there were clouds such as these (drawing on the blackboard) [table X, lower right], but they were not like our clouds today, which appear to be dead. On the contrary, they were living clouds, as alive as our plants are today. If you could imagine our clouds taking on life and turning greenish in color, then you would have an imaginative picture of what the plant kingdom looked like back then.

If you think that this is quite strange, then in this regard I might mention that there are some gentlemen in the field of science who are very funny. Recently you could read an article in the newspaper that might make you chuckle. Once again a new scientific discovery was being described in a style typical of today's science reporters. The scientist had determined that if milk has been prepared in a special way, it can be used to heal scurvy, a rather ugly disease. Well, gentlemen, what does such a scientist do nowadays? I've already directed your attention to this matter earlier. The scientist analyzes the milk. He discovers that milk consists of certain chemical ingredients. I also mentioned to you that if you give mice milk containing all these chemical ingredients, they will derive their nourishment from it and continue to live, but if you give them the ingredients separately, they will die after only a few days! This is what Professor Bunge's students also found out.[3] So they said to themselves, "There is simply this other element necessary for life right there in the milk and also in the honey. Let's call it a 'vitamin.'" You remember, I gave you this example once before. It's just as if you had said, "Poverty is due to pauperism." Likewise they say here that there is vitamin in the milk.

So they made a big discovery. In milk there are all sorts of chemical elements and compounds with very scholarly sounding names. And it is a fact that milk prepared in a certain way can be used to cure scurvy. But using a very learned, scientific method, they wanted to determine if you could heal scurvy by giving separately to patients who are sick with scurvy all these things with scholarly names attached to them. Well, they were not healed of anything, most of all not of scurvy. And this was true despite the fact that the patients were given all the constituents of milk! But when all the parts are kept together in

---

3. See footnote, page 42.

this specially prepared milk, then they can cure a person of scurvy. Each constituent by itself does not heal; only the total containing all the elements is capable of healing.

What is it that remains, the scientist conducting the experiment asks, if you remove separately all the constituents? The scientist subtracts each part one by one until nothing remains but does not allow for the fact that these constituents are all contained in an etheric body; the scientist continues removing all the parts. And what remains? By this account it is a vitamin! The vitamin that heals scurvy is not contained in anything that has been removed. So where is it? These people come with a nice idea—it's in the water that is in the milk, because it is not in all the other things that have been chemically analyzed. The conclusion then is that water is the missing compound that actually heals scurvy!

This is really quite funny, but today it is considered a very learned way of determining the truth. For if the water contains the vitamin, then we have come just about far enough with scholarly, scientific thinking that we could allow the clouds to be considered alive. Because then we would have to look outside and say that everywhere that there is water, there would also be vitamins in the water. We will have arrived at the point when the Earth was the way I have described it to you. The only problem is that it no longer is that way today.

Back then there was something I would like to call a "plant-hood," a plant-being, a single living covering of plants. And this living plant cover was fertilized everywhere by the surrounding environment. There also were no animals fixed in definite forms. No wasps existed either, but instead, out of the environment, there arose only a substance that had lived in an animal way. Our Earth once was in a condition that might be described this way. It was surrounded by clouds that contained plant life, and approaching these clouds from the periphery were other clouds; these other clouds, which were of an animal nature, fertilized the plant life clouds. The animalhood came from the cosmos, whereas the planthood came out of the Earth.

All of this has changed. The plants of that early time have become our flowers with their definite shapes and forms, flowers that now grow out of the Earth and do not form large clouds anymore. But something remained with these flowers—the fact that they want to experience an influence that comes to them from the environment. There, for example, is a rose that grows out of the Earth (drawing on blackboard) [table XI, page 166, left]. There is one rose leaf, and there is another, and so on. Then a wasp comes up to the rose. The wasp gnaws or cuts a piece out of the leaf, carries it back to its nest, and uses it to build or to give to its young ones for nourishment. The wasp simply bites off a piece and carries it away. As I've said, our rose plants today are no longer clouds; they have become in shape and form very sharply delineated things. But that part of the plant which once lived in the clouds and was connected with that which came to it from all directions in the form of animal nature, has, despite everything that has occurred in the meantime, remained in the rose's leaves and blossoms! It is situated right in there. In every rose leaf there is something that can do no other but be fertilized by the entire environment.

You see, gentlemen, these flowers need, which they very definitely require, a chemical substance that also plays an important role in the human body. If you analyze the human body chemically, you'll find various chemical substances. All these substances undergo continual changes. But everywhere these substances eventually are transformed into something that is always present in the human body. The human body needs this substance, which is formic acid.

If you go out to an anthill, collect ants, and squeeze them, you'll get a juice. This juice contains formic acid and some alcohol. This is the juice that is in ants. But you, too, have this juice very thinly distributed throughout your body. Whatever you eat as long as you are alive will always be changed—not exclusively, since there are other substances in smaller quantities—to formic acid. This formic acid fills your entire body. When you are ill and don't have sufficient formic acid, this situation is in itself something very bad for the body. For then your body will tend, just because it does not have enough formic acid in it—now I'm coming back to Mr. Müller's question, to give an answer to it—the body will tend to show signs of gout or rheumatism. The body is creating too much uric acid and not enough formic acid.

So it is that ants have in themselves the same thing that human beings need. But formic acid is, on the whole, something that is needed throughout all of nature. You won't be able to find the bark of any tree that doesn't contain some formic acid. Throughout the tree, just as throughout the human body, you'll find formic acid everywhere. In each leaf there has to be formic acid. However, it is not only formic acid that must be in there, but something related to formic acid, which is what wasps and also bees have within themselves, a chemical substance that they transform into bee poison. All these insects carry in themselves a certain chemical substance that is poisonous. If a bee stings you, you'll get an inflammation; if a wasp stings you, well, then some of you would have a rather bad experience. The entire matter of wasp stings is quite bad. Brehm relates an interesting episode that illustrates how such insects can play a terrible trick on both humans and animals.

This is close to how the story was told. A cowherd, still rather young, had quite a few cows in a pasture, and in this pasture there were various insect nests in many places. The cowherd's dog ran in circles. Suddenly the dog went crazy, and the cowherd had no idea what was wrong. The dog ran as fast as possible to a brook, jumped in, and kept shaking himself. The cowherd was completely bewildered by the dog's actions and tried to help him, but he came from another direction. He didn't jump into the brook, but tried to help the dog from the other side. Unfortunately, he had taken up a position on top of an insect nest, as very likely the dog also had done, and the insects began stinging him. Then he, too, ran around wildly and finally jumped into the brook as well. Since both the cowherd and the dog were gone, the cows gradually became confused and began to move about. Those cows that stepped on the insect nests were also stung and acted as if they were crazy. Finally, the greater portion of the herd ended up in the brook. Such insect stings can really create havoc. After all, these insects have something poisonous in them. And, finally, if you are bitten by an ant, there will also be a slight inflammation, because the ant will allow some formic acid to flow into the wound. Once again, formic acid is present in all living things in just the appropriate dilution.

Gentlemen, if there were no ants, no bees, and no wasps, those that actually prepare these poisons, what would happen? The very same thing would happen that would occur with the propagation of human beings if you suddenly decided to behead all men and allow only women to continue to exist here on Earth. Humanity would not be able to continue to propagate because there would be no male seed. Well, these insects all still have some additional seed; nevertheless, what comes from these poisons has become necessary for their continued life. This is because these poisons have been left over from that which used to be in the environment of the Old Moon. Very finely distributed, bee poison, wasp poison, and formic acid (ant poison) originated in the cosmos and came down over the plants. What remains of it is still present today. If you go out and see a bee sitting somewhere on a willow tree or on a flower, then you don't say that the insect is simply robbing the flower. Instead you say that while the little bee is sitting on it and obtaining nectar, the flower is having such a pleasant experience that it sends its own plant juice toward the place where the bee is sucking it out.

This is very interesting, gentlemen! As the bee is sucking, the flower allows its juice to flow to that spot. And in this same stream of flowing juice, while the bee is removing something from the flower, bee poison also flows in the opposite direction from the bee to the flower. And while the gall wasp is stinging, wasp poison flows into the plant. And, in particular, when an ant crawls over a plant, even over the dead portions of it, like the bark, it allows formic acid to flow into it. When an ant crawls on a flower, flower juice combines with formic acid. This is necessary. If this didn't happen, and if there weren't any bees, wasps, and ants, which continually come into contact with the world of flowers and nibble at them, then the necessary formic acid and the other necessary poisons wouldn't flow toward these flowers, and the flowers would have to die out after a certain period of time.

You see, such chemicals, normally called the substances of life—well, these we highly treasure above all others. But, in reality, only such substances as formic acid are the true substances of life. If you examine the deadly nightshade, or belladonna, you will see that there is a poison, a deadly poison in it. But what is it that this plant is doing? Specifically, it is collecting a spiritual element present in the cosmic environment. Poisons generally are the collectors of such spiritual elements. For this very reason, poisons can also serve as remedies used to effect a cure. And understood on a very basic level, flowers are continually getting sicker and sicker, and these little bees, wasps, and ants continually play the role of doctor, bringing formic acid to the flowers, which they need in order to be healed completely again. You see, these bees, wasps, and ants are not simply robbers; at the same time, they bring to the flowers the possibility of remaining alive.

And it is the same with the caterpillars. They would die out, would simply not exist anymore after a certain period of time. Well, you might say, that wouldn't be such a great loss; this type of caterpillar would simply become extinct. But then you need to consider that birds eat them and so forth. All of nature is interrelated in this way. When we observe, for example, that ants penetrate everything with their formic acid, we have obtained an insight into the inner workings of nature's ecosystem. This is something that is truly very grand. Everywhere things are happening that are absolutely necessary for maintaining life and the existence of this world.

You see, there is a tree (drawing on blackboard) [table XI, middle]. The tree has its bark. Then the bark begins to rot, after I've cut it down. There is the mold. Now people say, "Just let it rot." So the people calmly stand by and watch everything that remains in the woods simply rot away. And what is it that doesn't rot away during the course of a year? Leaves and similar matter. People just let all these things decompose. But in nature these substances have been organized differently. Everywhere in the vicinity there are anthills. Originating from these anthills [table XI, upper right], formic acid finds its way into the forest soil.

If you have the floor of a forest over here and an anthill over there, it would be the same as taking a glass full of water and putting a drop of something into it. It immediately expands to fill the entire glass. If you put salt into it, all of the water at once becomes salty [table XI, lower right]. If you have an anthill there, then the formic acid seeps in similar fashion into the floor of the forest. The entire forest floor, which is dying off, becomes saturated with this formic acid. In this way, formic acid reaches the forest floor, which is dying off, but it also penetrates the living plants. We have also considered how a plant takes up formic acid or bee or wasp poison, as, for instance, when a bee sits on a flower and the flower sucks up what it can get from the bee, and we have also considered how a caterpillar needs formic acid. It is possible to determine all these things only if you learn to apply the methods of anthroposophic science. Traditional physical science is concerned only with that which the bee takes away from the flower. But bees wouldn't have been able to sit on flowers for the past few thousand years if they hadn't cultivated them by nibbling at them to keep them healthy.

The same is true for all the lifeless material you can find in the forest. Imagine, gentlemen, even today's physical science, at the state of knowledge it has now, assumes that the time will come when everything on Earth will be completely dead. It would have to say this, because at some time in the future a condition would be reached when material destroyed by mold would prevail and the Earth would have to be considered dead. But this time will not come because the Earth's soil, wherever it has become moldy, is saturated with that which the bees, wasps, and ants give it. To be sure, bees give it only to living flowers and wasps almost always to living flowers. But ants also give in what they transmit as formic acid something directly to rotten, dead material, and by doing this, they stimulate life to a certain degree, and they contribute to the fact that the Earth in its decaying substance remains alive at all. You could really say that the spirit that is present and prevails in all these things is certainly one to be marveled at. But as you examine this matter more closely, you can see that it all has great significance.

Let's now look at the agricultural ants that set up their little fields, where they grow and tend their plants very differently. It is true that a human being would not be able to exist on the amount of food they grow there. For if a human being were to try to eat these little rice kernels that are as hard as pebbles, the person would, first of all, become strangely ill from ingesting too much formic acid. But besides this, the individual would probably break off some teeth so that a dentist would have to work hard for some time to repair them. After that the person would experience a miserable death—all because of eating these pebble-hard rice kernels that the ants have prepared in this manner.

But the ants, more accurately the entire ant colony, says to itself, "If we simply go out into the open fields of nature and suck out of the plants that substance which we find present everywhere, then we will not be able to create within ourselves sufficient formic acid, and as a result we won't be able to give enough to the Earth, which depends on it. So we'll do it this way: We'll choose specific plants, which we will grow and harvest in such a way that the resulting food will be very tightly compressed, pressed together so much that it becomes as hard as stone, and from this we'll be able to extract a large amount of formic acid." These agricultural ants do this in order to produce as much formic acid as they possibly can. And these particular ants are the ones that manage to put a lot of formic acid back into the soil. This is the connection I've wanted you to see.

In this way you will also understand that poisons, even though they create inflammations or similar conditions, also function as chemicals that have continuous curative powers that stave off the process of dying. You could also say that the bee, in particular, is extremely important in this regard. The bee helps maintain the existence of the flowers; it keeps them from dying out. This is why there is such a deep relationship between bees and flowers.

This maintenance of life becomes evident every time insects move about, carrying on their activities on the Earth. When this happens, I would like to say that the Earth has had its store of poisons replenished, which means, of course, that death has been prevented and life has been maintained. This is the spiritual connection. When someone asks what the spiritual connections are, I never like to say that it is simply this or that way, but rather I prefer to present the facts and then let a person decide, based upon the facts, whether the connections make sense or not. The facts are usually arrayed in such a manner that you will see that there is significance and meaning in all of them. Unfortunately, those who consider themselves true scholars don't really tell you this. But in life this does play a certain role. In the areas where we live, less respect will perhaps be accorded to all that I have said, but as you go farther south, you will hear farmers, simple people, say out of instinctive knowledge, "These ant colonies—you must not disturb them because they keep mold from becoming too destructive." And the very smart ones also say something else. If you go for a walk with them through the woods, where trees have been harvested and young trees are beginning to grow, these people, using their noses—they are very smart with their noses—walk through such an area and come to a place where they say, "Well, that's going to grow very well. The moldy odor is not as strong here, so there must be an ant colony nearby that is doing its job." This is what such people can smell. Based on a finely attuned sense of smell, many a farmers' saying has been formulated that has proved to be very useful.

Unfortunately, our modern civilization has become too much of a brain-oriented culture, where the mechanical, abstract aspects of thinking are emphasized, much to the detriment of these instinctive methods, which now have become simply words and nothing else. These creatures, specifically when they appear as collective groups, as in the beehive or ant colony, know all of this. This knowledge is obtained through a very special sense of smell. And, as I've said, much of the instinctive knowledge that human beings have is based upon the intelligence of the nose.

Next week we will continue this discussion. The main point I had wanted to make today is that bees, wasps, and ants do not simply remove something from nature, an activity that makes them appear to be robbers, but they also give nature the possibility to continue living and thriving.

• Lecture Eight

Dornach, December 22, 1923

Good morning, gentlemen! We need to continue speaking about Mr. Dollinger's question. He had posed this question for you—and I'm sure all of you will find this to be of interest—of what the connection is, on a spiritual level, between the entire horde of insects that goes to the plants and that which is in the plants.

You see, gentlemen, I said earlier that everywhere around us are not only elements such as oxygen and nitrogen, but there is present throughout nature also intelligence and understanding. Nobody is astonished if you say, "We inhale the air"—because the air is all around us and because the scientific explanation that is now printed in every schoolbook tells us that air is everywhere and that we breathe in this air. But I have known, for example, people out in the country who thought this was a figment of the imagination; they simply didn't know that air is everywhere, the same way that people today don't know that the power of mind is present around us in nature. They are the ones who consider it a bit of fantasy if you say that in the same way we inhale air with the help of our lungs, we also "inhale" this power of mind, for example, with our noses or ears. And I've given you numerous examples by which you can see that the power of mind is present everywhere. Last time we spoke about a particularly interesting chapter of natural science, about bees, wasps, and ants. Perhaps there is no better place in nature to obtain such a thorough insight into the inner workings of nature than in the activities of insects. Insects just happen to be truly remarkable creatures, and they will in the future still reveal quite a few secrets to us.

It is worth noting that we are discussing insects at the same time that we are celebrating the hundredth anniversary of the famous scientist specializing in insect research, Jean-Henri Fabre, who was born a century ago on December 22 and lived at just the time when materialism began pervading science.[1] For this reason he interpreted everything materialistically, but he did bring to light a great many facts about the life of insects. For this reason it is natural that we think of him as we discuss insects today.

First I would like to give you an example of a type of insect that you will find interesting because of its connection with bees. A bee achieves a high degree of perfection in the work that it accomplishes. The most remarkable thing about a bee is not that it produces honey but that it can produce completely out of itself, out of its own body, these wonderfully constructed honeycomb cells. It has to carry into the beehive whatever it uses as building materials. It works in such a way that it doesn't use this material in the original form, but rather brings it into the beehive already completely transformed. The bee does this all by itself, and what it creates comes directly out of itself.

There is, however, another genus of bee, which doesn't accomplish its tasks in the same way as the common honeybee does. The unique method employed by this bee demonstrates the tremendous power of mind, or intelligence, that exists in all of nature. Let's observe for a moment the work

---

1. Jean-Henri Fabre, 1823-1915, French scholar and researcher specializing in insects; his main work was *Souvenirs entomologiques: Études sur l'instinct et mœurs des insectes*, 10 vols., 1879-1907.

methods of this type of bee, normally called the wood bee (*Xyolocopa violacea*) and not as highly regarded as the common honeybee because it can be a nuisance for human beings.[2] This is an extremely industrious bee, a bee that must really overcome difficult circumstances in order to ensure its survival—not the survival of the individual bee but of the entire genus. This animal looks for wood that no longer is part of a tree but has been cut and processed for use elsewhere. You can find this wood bee with its nests, which I'll describe for you shortly, anywhere you have a wooden plug or peg that has been hammered into the ground or somewhere else. Such pieces of dead wood as serve to hold down tents or to create wooden columns and also wooden garden benches or garden doors can serve as likely nesting sites. In there you'll find the wood bee.

Imagine that this is such a post (drawing on the blackboard) [table XII, page 167, left]. This also is wood that no longer serves as part of a tree. Now along comes the wood bee and drills an entry hole into the post at an angle. When the bee makes it all the way into the center, has removed all the excess wood pieces, and has enlarged the entrance to become a bit more like a channel, it begins to drill in a completely different direction. It drills in such a way that a small, ring-shaped chamber is formed. Then the insect flies away, brings back all sorts of materials from nearby, and lines the chamber with these wadding materials. When it is finished, it lays an egg in there, from which a larva will emerge. This egg lies there in the chamber. After having laid the egg, the little bee makes a lid, in the center of which there is a hole. It continues drilling above this lid and fashions a second chamber for another larva to use as its living space. After having lined the chamber with wadding, laid a second egg, and provided

2. See note at end of lecture, pp. 159-161.

a lid with a hole in it, the bee continues to the next chamber and so on until it has made ten or twelve such chambers, one on top of the other. In each one there is an egg.

The larvae can develop inside the wood. Into each chamber the bee has placed food for each larva. The larva eats the food that has been prepared for it and grows until it is mature enough to crawl out. But now the time comes when the insect changes into a chrysalis, then becomes a bee with wings and wants to fly from the nest. When this mature insect wants to leave 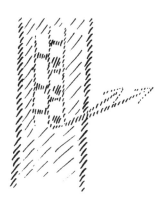 the nest, it must depart via the original entrance corridor. Here we see evidence of the cleverness of the wood bee, in that the mature insect can leave the nest using the passageway that had been drilled out first. That's fine so far. But when the second insect, which is younger than the first, and then the third, the egg of which was laid even more recently, and so on, want to leave, these later insects, for whom living quarters were constructed later by the mother bee, will not be able to find an exiting passageway because only one such entrance or exit was drilled out. An awkward situation now arises, because those bees confined to the upper chambers would be doomed to die eventually, since there is no easy way out for them.

The mother averts this catastrophe by creating the little holes in the lids, which the younger insects can find and through which they can let themselves drop before crawling out of the main entrance. The bee from the third egg, after it has developed sufficiently, drops through the two holes made for the lower chambers, where the previous residents, who are older and have already matured and then escaped, no longer live. In this way the younger insects do not disturb those in the chambers below, which are now empty since the insects once there have matured and left. There is never any contact between them because the older ones are not there.

You see, the entire nest has been planned with such great wisdom and foresight that you can't help but be astonished. When people today mechanically try to reproduce things, they are usually created in imitation, but the result is often not as skillfully made as nature would do it. Things as they exist in nature are created with extraordinary skill, and you would have to admit that there is definitely evidence of intelligence and understanding. You could find hundreds or even thousands of examples to illustrate this point by examining how insects build and how they act when they are at work. Just consider how much knowledge and understanding is evidenced by the agricultural ants in the agricultural operation that I told you about recently.

We also observed another matter as we were looking at these bees, wasps, and ants. I told you that these creatures have a substance in them that is poisonous, and that this poisonous substance is, at the same time, an excellent medicine, if the proper dose is determined and prescribed. Bee poison is an exceptional medicine with curative powers, as is wasp poison. And formic acid, which ants secrete, is an even better medicine. And I've indicated something else to you—we can get this formic acid by disturbing an anthill, collecting the ants, and then squeezing them. Mainly we obtain formic acid from ants, but if you knew, relatively speaking, how much formic acid is in this hall, you would be very astonished! You would say, "We certainly can't look for an anthill here in a corner of this hall." Gentlemen, just as you sit there, you are truly an anthill yourselves! For everywhere in your arms and legs, muscles and other tissues, heart, lung, liver, spleen—everywhere you'll find formic acid. To be sure, it's not as concentrated or strong as you'll find in an anthill. But even so you are completely saturated with formic acid. Yes, this is something very strange.

Why do we have this formic acid in our bodies? You can determine whether a person has too little of it. If someone appears before you with an illness—actually most human beings are just a bit sick—this person might have any of a hundred different illnesses that all look alike externally. You need to recognize what this sick person is actually lacking; the fact that a person is pale or unable to eat, these are only superficial signs. You need to determine what it is that is really lacking. With some people it is simply that they don't have enough of the anthill in themselves, that they don't generate enough formic acid. The same way in which the anthill produces formic acid, the body must make formic acid all over, but particularly in the spleen. If a person produces an insufficient amount of formic acid, such an individual needs to be given a medicinal preparation, a remedy, by means of which you help externally create enough formic acid within the body.

But it is important to notice the changes that take place in a person who just happens to have too little formic acid. These observations can only be made when those who wish to observe these matters truly have a thorough understanding of human nature. You need to create a clear picture in your mind of what is going on in a person's soul, a person who, at first, has had sufficient formic acid within and then later has too little of this substance. This is truly remarkable. Such a person will tell you, if you ask in the correct way, the right things about the illness. Assume, for instance, you have before you an individual who tells you, after being inspired to think along certain lines, "Several months ago I could remember just about everything. I could think back and reflect on past occurrences very well. Now I have trouble with that; I don't seem to be able to do it anymore. Every time I try to think back, I just can't remember."

Gentlemen, this is often a much more important indication than all the results of external medical tests can give you, tests that you naturally should also undertake. Today you can test urine for the albumen content, for pus, for sugar, and for other constituents, and you'll get rather interesting results. But under certain circumstances, it can be much more important that a person describes a symptom such as suffering from memory loss. For when an individual tells you something like that, you will naturally have to obtain more information, and then you might come to the following conclusion. In the most recent period of this person's life, the level of formic acid in the body has decreased to the point of becoming insufficient for supporting certain important functions.

Now someone who still thinks on an external level could say, "This person doesn't have enough formic acid within. Either I'll squeeze some ants to get formic acid or I'll create it synthetically in a laboratory; then I'll administer formic acid in an appropriate dose." You can do this for a period of time, but the patient will come to you later and say, "But this stuff didn't help me one bit." What is the situation here? It really doesn't help the patient at all. The diagnosis was absolutely correct; the person didn't have enough formic acid in the system. You administered formic acid, and it didn't do any good at all. So what do we have going on here?

You see, if you research this matter, you'll discover the real explanation. The formic acid doesn't help a particular individual, but with others it is always successful. After a while you begin to notice the difference. In the case of those patients whom the formic acid helped, you will find that they show evidence of a mucous obstruction in the lungs. The other patients, who derive no benefit from the formic acid as a medication, are those in whom you will discover mucous obstructions in the liver, kidneys, or spleen. This turns out to be a rather peculiar situation. There is a great difference between an insufficient amount of formic acid in the lungs and the same situation in the liver. The difference exists by virtue of the fact that the lung can immediately use the formic acid that comes from an ant colony, but the liver can't do anything at all with it.

And now here is something else, gentlemen! If you notice that a person has a problem with the liver, or specifically the intestines, and formic acid doesn't help at all, then you'll have to dispense oxalic acid. That means that you'll have to press the juice out of the common wood sorrel, or from clover that grows in the fields, derive the acid from it, and give it as medicine. So you see, if a person has a problem with the lungs, you need to give formic acid; if a person has a problem with the liver or intestines, you have to give oxalic acid. The strange thing, however, is that the person to whom you give oxalic acid will, after a certain amount of time, begin to produce formic acid within! What's really important is that you don't simply administer from outside the patient things that you want the patient to take as medicine, but rather you really must know what the human organism will do with this remedy on its own. If you give formic acid, then the organism will say, "That's not for me. I want to do the work by myself." (In this case you administered the formic acid already prepared for the body to use directly.) "There's no work involved in it for me; I'll not get it up into the lungs." Naturally, you have to give this medication in such a manner that it will go into the stomach. In the end it will get into the intestines. At this point, the human organism tells the body that is ready to do its work: "What are you giving me here? You mean to tell me that I'm not supposed to create formic acid by myself first but that you want me to take this formic acid that you put into the stomach and convey it to the lungs where it is needed? No, I refuse to do it." The human organism really wants to have oxalic acid, so that it can transform it into formic acid on its own.

Yes, gentlemen, life involves work, not substances, and the most important thing to know is that life doesn't consist at all in simply eating cabbage, turnips, or beets but rather in what the body must do when the cabbage, turnip, or beet substances are taken into the digestive system. In any case, the body must not produce cabbage all over again from the cabbage that has just arrived in the digestive system. This is, remarkably, the very thing that is at the basis of our present-day civilization.

But you'll see from this example what an unusual relationship exists within nature. Out there are the plants. The clover plant has been defined in the German language in a very special way—Kleesäure literally means "acid from clover." But actually clover acid, or oxalic acid, is found in all plants; it is simply that its greatest concentration is in the clover plant. That's why we talk about "clover acid" in German. Just as you will find formic acid (in German this is called "ant acid" or "acid from ants," since ants supply it in concentrated form) everywhere in nature and everywhere in the human body; likewise you will find everywhere in nature and in the human body Kleesäure, or oxalic acid.

Now here is another very interesting fact. Take the following experiment. You have a retort, the kind you find in a chemical laboratory. You place a flame under it and introduce some oxalic acid into this retort—this is a salty, crumbly ash—then add the same quantity of glycerin. You mix these constituents together and heat them. The steamy vapors will move over here (drawing on the blackboard) [table XII], and you will be able to collect at the open end whatever comes out. But at the same time that this is happening, you notice that air is escaping, escaping all over. When you examine and analyze this escaping air, you find out that it is carbon dioxide. So carbon dioxide is escaping, and here, where you are collecting what is coming over, you have formic acid. Now there's formic acid, but in the retort you had oxalic acid and glycerin. The glycerin remains and the other part moves over; the liquid formic acid drops down over here, and the carbon dioxide escapes at this point.

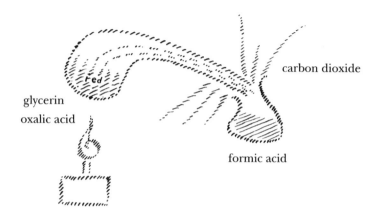

Now take a very good look at this whole procedure. Assume for a moment that instead of a retort you had the human liver before you or, let's say, any human or animal tissue (drawing on the blackboard) [table XII, upper middle], any organ located in the animal abdomen, liver, spleen, or another organ of that type. Through the stomach I introduce oxalic acid. The body has, by itself, glycerin. So then I have in my intestines both oxalic acid and glycerin. And what happens? Now examine the human mouth; that is where the carbon dioxide escapes and the formic acid drops down from the lungs in every direction toward the other organs in the human body. So this whole process that I have sketched for you is really taking place in our own bodies. We are constantly producing formic acid from oxalic acid in our bodies.

Now think of all the plants that are found all over the Earth. In all of them you'll find oxalic acid. And think of the insects. In the case of insects the facts emerge in a very remarkable way. Think, first of all, of the ants. They go to these plants or to the rotting material that comes from plants. Everywhere, in all these things, there is oxalic acid, and these animals, just as humans do themselves, make formic acid from them. This formic acid is present everywhere. Insects make it possible for formic acid to be present everywhere.

Yes, a philistine will look into the air and say that in the air there is nitrogen and oxygen. But, gentlemen, there is always formic acid present in a very small amount, because the insects fly through the air. What this means is that we have on one side the human being. The human being is a microcosm, a little world or universe. A person creates formic acid within and saturates the breath continually with formic acid. And in the macrocosm, in the great world or universe, the process that takes place within the human being is replaced by the whole army of insects. The great breath of air that surrounds the entire Earth is saturated with the formic acid that is created from the oxalic acid present in plants. It really happens this way [table XIII, page 167]. If you observe correctly and examine the lower part of the body of a human being with the stomach, liver, kidneys, spleen, and intestines, you will find that it is true that oxalic acid is continually being transformed into formic acid in these organs. This formic acid enters along with the air a person inhales, and in this way it is distributed to all the parts of the body. This is what goes on in human beings.

On this Earth, you have plants everywhere. Then you have in various forms the insects that fly over it. Down there you have oxalic acid. The insects fly to the plants and make contact with them. Through this contact formic acid is created and spreads throughout the air, so that we also breathe in formic acid that is present in the air around us. That which the wasps have is a poison very similar to formic acid, only partially transformed. That which bees carry around in their stingers—actually the entire body of the bee possesses it—is also transformed formic acid, but transformed to a higher degree. When you examine this, you come to say to yourself, "We look at these insects—ants, wasps, bees—and find that they are doing a very smart thing. Why are they doing something that appears to show so much intelligence? If the ant didn't have any formic acid, it would accomplish all those marvelous things, which I have described for you, in a rather stupid manner. Only because ants are created in such a way that they can produce formic acid does everything that they construct seem so full of understanding and reason. The same is true for wasps and bees.

Doesn't this give us occasion to say to ourselves, if we also produce this formic acid within ourselves, that in nature understanding and knowledge are found everywhere? This is all due to formic acid. We also have understanding and knowledge within us because we have formic acid. Formic acid would not exist if it weren't for oxalic acid being present beforehand. And so the little insects flutter about the plants and are the reason why the oxalic acid in plants is changed into formic acid or, if you will, undergoes a metamorphosis.

These are the things you begin to understand only if you now ask yourself what the situation is with oxalic acid. You see, oxalic acid is present everywhere where there is life. Wherever something is alive, there is oxalic acid. But there is also an etheric body. One function that the etheric body carries out is that it immediately renews oxalic acid. However, oxalic acid will never become formic acid of a type that a human or animal organism can use unless the astral body transforms the oxalic acid into formic acid. For it is a fact that the formic acid that is derived from the process in the retort is a formic acid that will be of no benefit to the human or animal body. You'll be deceived if you believe that it can really help at all, because in reality it is dead. The formic acid created in humans and by insects is alive, and it appears wherever sensations and feelings arise and the soul element is present. A human being must develop formic acid within if such a person wants to generate the soul element from the basic level of life processes that exist in the lower body, where oxalic acid plays a very important role. Then the soul element lives in the formic acid of the breath and rises to the head, where it can continue to function and become effective. The soul element needs this process that converts oxalic acid into formic acid within a human being.

What really happens when the oxalic acid is converted into formic acid? You see, the first thing that I told you about can give you the answer. This wood bee I spoke about is very interesting in this regard just because it works its way into wood that no longer has life in it. If this wood bee could not properly use the wood, it would probably seek its nest elsewhere. It doesn't bore its nest into living trees but rather into already rotting wood; wherever posts begin to rot is a place where it lays its eggs after it has constructed its nest.

If you study the connection between rotting material and the wood bees, you'll eventually find out that the same process that occurs in rotting wood also takes place continually in the human body. It begins to rot, and if it rots too much it dies. The process that takes place in nature is the same one a human being must carry out—a person needs to construct cells. This is something an individual can do only by transforming plant material that is saturated with oxalic acid into formic acid, into a substance that is saturated with formic acid.

Now you can ask what significance this whole process has for nature. Well, gentlemen, let's imagine a wooden post that is decaying. People would prefer that a wood bee never come near their posts, since these bees usually spread out quite a bit within the post, and the next year this post would probably fall over because the bees have hollowed it out. People may not really like this very much, but nature loves this process all the more for the benefits it derives from it. For if all the wood that comes from plants were to continue its existence without these bees' nests, the wood would eventually—you can watch this process as things rot—crumble, fall to dust, and become entirely useless material. However, the wood in which a wood bee has worked does not simply get scattered about, but, on the contrary, it takes on "life" again. And from all this wood that has been slightly enlivened again by these wood bees and, for that matter, likewise by other insects, much of that material will arise that will keep the Earth from decaying completely, from becoming a cloud of dust in space. This material will make it possible for the Earth to continue its life, because it is constantly being restored to life by these insects. As human beings, we inhale formic acid, but in nature the formic acid that is prepared by insects from the oxalic acid of plants functions in such a way that it becomes the only way to make possible the continued existence of the Earth at all.

Now examine the connection between these things. Here we have the human being and here the Earth [table XIII]. Let's look at the human being first. Let's assume it's a young child. As long as this child is still young, it can transform very easily the oxalic acid located in the lower body into formic acid. The organs get enough formic acid. The human soul develops within the child. So here we have formic acid as the foundation for soul and spirit. And when a human becomes old and can't develop enough formic acid anymore, the soul and spirit leave. It's the formic acid that attracts and mobilizes soul and spirit; otherwise the spirit will go away. This is very interesting.

If, for example, you observe properly a person with very many internal purulent infections, you'll find it is true that formic acid will help such a person overcome these infections. Then the proper relationship between the astral body and the physical body will reestablish itself, a relationship that was disturbed and hindered by the infections. We can say that formic acid is always used in the proper way as the foundation for soul and spirit. If the body just happens to have too little formic acid, it will decay and will no longer be able to support the soul; the body ages, and the soul must leave. Now we have the human being on one side here, and on the other side is nature. In nature as well, formic acid is derived continuously from oxalic acid, so that the Earth constantly has the possibility of being surrounded not only by oxygen and nitrogen but also by formic acid [table XIII].

This formic acid makes it possible for the Earth not to "die off" completely each year but instead to be able to resuscitate itself year after year. What is located beneath the Earth as seed has a longing for formic acid. And this is what the process of rejuvenation consists of. Every winter the spirit of the Earth is itself striving to leave or simply go away, and in spring it restores itself to life again. The spirit of the Earth causes the Earth to become rigid and stiff in winter; in spring it enlivens the Earth once more. This happens because that which waits under the Earth as seed comes into contact with the formic acid that had been created the previous year by the interaction of the insect world with the plant world. The seeds develop, grow, and make contact not only with oxygen, nitrogen, and carbon dioxide but also with formic acid. This formic acid stimulates them to develop oxalic acid once again by themselves, which in turn makes it possible for formic acid to be present the next year. But just as formic acid in a human being can provide the basis for the presence of soul and spirit, so, likewise, the formic acid that is spread out over the cosmos provides the foundation for the presence of the Earth's spiritual and soul element. Now we can say that in the case of the Earth, formic acid is also the basis for the Earth's soul and the Earth's spirit [table XIII].

It is actually more difficult to transmit a telegram in a region where there are not ant colonies than it is in a region where they exist, because the electricity and the magnetism needed for telegraphy depend upon formic acid. When the telegraph wires go through a city where there are no ants, the power to accomplish transmission must come from the countryside, where the wires pass through the fields, so that the magnetic and electric current will make its way through the cities at all. But naturally, formic acid spreads itself out and also fills the air that exists in the cities.

Well, gentlemen, now you see that we can say that whatever is contained within a human being—with regard to the production of formic acid as well—also exists in nature. A human being is a microcosm, a small world. It is uniquely the case with a human being that throughout life until death, a person possesses the capacity to make formic acid from oxalic acid. But then a human being loses this capability, and the physical body dies. Then the human soul has to wait before once again receiving a body, which in a child properly transforms oxalic acid into formic acid. With nature this process continues on and on: winter, summer, winter, summer. The oxalic acid is always transformed into formic acid.

If you carefully observe a dying individual, you'll get the feeling that there is an effort on the part of this person, even in the process of dying, to find out whether the body is still capable of creating formic acid. Then, at the point when the body is no longer capable of the task, death takes over. A human being goes into the spirit world and can't endure any longer being in the body. We can say that a human being dies at a certain point in time, and after a long period of time comes back in another body. Meanwhile this person is in the spirit world.

When a young queen emerges in a beehive, as I've told you, there is something that disturbs the bees. Up until this event, the bees have been living in what might be called a twilight. Then they see the young queen giving off a light. What is connected with the shining of this young queen? What is connected with it is that the young queen is taking away the power of the bee poison that the old queen possesses. And this, gentlemen, is the great fear of a swarm that leaves its hive—it is afraid that it no longer possesses bee poison, a state that means that it can't defend itself anymore or save itself. So it moves away from this disturbing source, the young queen. In the same way that the human soul leaves the body when it can't get enough formic acid, the older bees also leave when there is an insufficient amount of altered formic acid—bee poison—present. And if you now look at a swarm of bees, it is, to be sure, visible, but it really looks like the soul of a human being, a soul that is forced to leave its body. This is truly a grand sight, to see a horde of bees swarming away. In the same way in which the human soul leaves the body, so also does the old queen, after a young queen reaches adulthood, leave the hive with her company. You can really see, by looking at the escaping swarm of bees, an image of the human soul flying away from the body.

Oh, gentlemen, this is a grand sight to behold! There's only a slight difference, in that the human soul has never reached the point of developing its powers sufficiently to create these little creatures. Within us there is continually the tendency to want to do this; we want to become many tiny creatures. We actually have within ourselves a tendency to continually want to change the form of things inside our bodies so that they become like crawling bacilli or bacteria, or like little bees, but we suppress this process before it happens. In so doing we become complete human beings and not a collection of tiny entities. But the beehive is not a complete human being. Bees can't find their way into the spirit world. We have to take them to an empty beehive to bring about a rebirth, or reincarnation, of these bees. This is very directly a picture of reincarnating human beings. That person who can observe such a phenomenon develops a tremendous respect for these old swarming bees with their queen, a swarm that acts the way it does because it is trying to find its way into the spiritual world. But this swarm has become so caught up in the material world, so physical, that it can no longer fulfill this desire. So the bees cuddle up together and become a single body. They want very much to be together. They want to leave this world. And you also know that while they are flying about, they might attach themselves to a tree trunk or something similar, and then they press themselves together in order to disappear, because they want to gain entrance into the spirit world. And then they once again become a proper colony when we help them by bringing them back to their new beehive.

So from this description you could probably say that insects teach us nothing short of what might be considered the highest understanding we can derive from nature. This is why looking at plants always enlightened the people of antiquity, who still had an instinctive sense for those things that I've been explaining to you, matters that present-day science has lost sight of completely. Back then people looked upon plants in a very special way. In our day, people are sometimes reminded of some of these things, for instance, when they bring home a fir tree and make a Christmas tree out of it. Then people are reminded of the fact that the way things are in nature can also become something important in the lives of human beings, can be something that can have an effect on our social lives. It's supposed to be a symbol for love, this fir tree transformed into a Christmas tree.

People generally believe that the idea of a Christmas tree is very old. But the fir tree was first used as a Christmas tree probably only one hundred and fifty to two hundred years ago. Before that time this custom didn't exist. But people did use a type of bush at Christmas. For example, during the Christmas plays that were performed in villages as early as the fifteenth and sixteenth centuries, there was someone who ran about advertising the play and also carried in his hand what might be considered a Christmas tree.[3] But this was the so-called Kranewittbaum, a term known only in Middle Germany; in reality this tree is the juniper, which has wonderful berries. Back then people took a juniper to serve as a Christmas tree. Why? Because the juniper berries that birds so much like to eat showed them the slight effect of poison that arises and must be penetrated by the Earth element so that the spiritual element might arise within it. The same way that the ant is drawn to wooden material or the wood bee goes to posts, another, much weaker acid is produced all over every morning by the bird picking at the berries on the juniper. The people of antiquity knew this instinctively and said to themselves that during winter, when the juniper stands there and the birds come to pick its berries, the Earth is once again rejuvenated, reenlivened by means of the juniper. From this natural phenomenon people formed a picture in their minds, one with a moral sense: Christ is reenlivening the Earth.

---

3. This refers to the traditional Christmas plays from Oberufer. See *Christmas Plays from Oberufer* (Bristol, U.K.: Rudolf Steiner Press, 1993).

So now we can already say: Looking at things in a properly natural way, we can see in all the processes of nature, symbols and representations of those things that occur in human life. People long ago looked at the birds sitting in a juniper with the same love as people today have when they see little Christmas cookies or the presents under the Christmas tree. The juniper was for these people a kind of Christmas tree that they carried into their homes. So it is that a juniper was made into something like a Christmas tree.

Now we need to come to a conclusion. I didn't want to allow today's session to pass by—I know this is a very stressful time for all of you—without having spoken about a very important subject. And we made it all the way to some thoughts about a bush that might really be looked upon as a Christmas tree, the juniper, which offers to birds the same things that plants offer to bees and that wood offers to ants and wood bees and, generally, to all insects. Finally, I would like to take this opportunity to wish you all a very happy, joyful, inwardly uplifting Christmas.

We'll let you know when the next lecture will be; it will be sometime in the near future.

Note in reference to the wood bee, page 142:
"With a loud buzzing sound, the female bee, having made it through the winter, flies out to search for a suitable home for its progeny among the boards of a stockade fence, lath work, or wooden posts. Any old wood—a rotting post, a brittle tree trunk with its bark falling off—will do for the difficult task this bee needs to complete. With great diligence this bee gnaws a hole into the wood about as large as the circumference of its body. It then penetrates several annual rings of the wood before it begins boring downward. The excess wood is removed as it

bores deeper and deeper, creating a tube or channel that can attain the length of one foot before it begins bending in a somewhat outward direction again. This mother allows herself only occasional breaks, during which time she flies to nearby flowers to obtain honey nectar to restore her energies. She finishes her tubelike chamber before the end of May. In the lowest part she places a mixture of honey nectar and pollen, upon which she lays a single egg. Then measuring upward to a height that approximates the circumference of the tube, she creates a lid made of concentric rings of kneaded sawdust. Thus the first cell has been closed off, making it possible to place another cell above it. This cell has the same dimensions as the first, and another egg is placed into it before it, too, is sealed off with a lid. This process is repeated over and over without interruption until an entire column of cells is formed.

"After a few days, the young maggot emerges from the egg. It lies in a curved position and takes up almost all the space in the cell by the time that it matures to the next stage about three weeks later. Then it spins a cocoon and changes into a chrysalis. Since the lowermost egg was the earliest laid, it will be the first to reach maturity; the second would be next, and the uppermost would be last. Will the first egg wait to mature until all its siblings have achieved their maturity before it makes its way out of this prison? There is no way that it will wait that long. It is situated standing on its head and will have to move only slightly forward, where it will discover that the cell wall will yield and break open. Then it will continue until it reaches the end of the curve, which is filled with loose wood materials somewhat similar to sawdust. Then it gnaws away the thin layer separating it from the warm summer air. The second one that crawls out follows the first, until all the siblings have emerged by the end of July or the beginning of August. The nest is now empty" (Jean-Henri Fabre, *Souvenirs entomologiques: Études sur l'instinct et mœurs des insectes*, pp. 484-485).

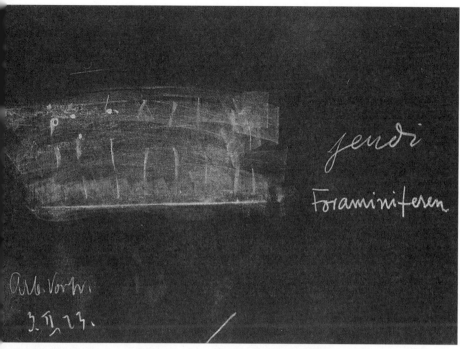

TABLE I

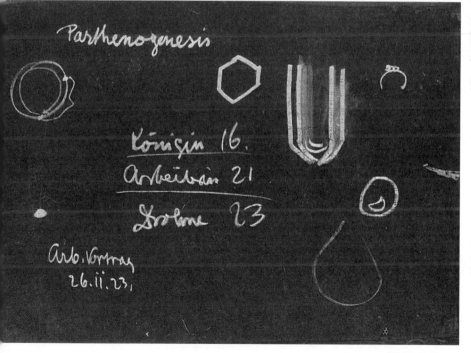

TABLE II

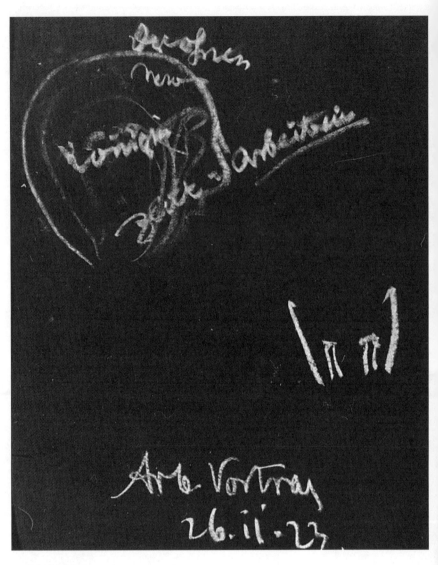

TABLE III

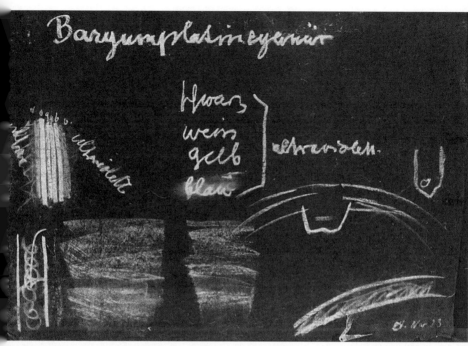

TABLE IV

Barymmplatinccyanür

Hwarz
weiss
gelb
blau
} schwanken.

Vitamin

23. März ——— 23. April ——— 11   73% 75%
        H   V   11   55% 74%
vis Comica   14   70% 88%

10
10
13
7
11
14
12
9
7

Casein
Fell
Zucker
Salzen

Arb. Vortrag 1.12.23.

TABLE V

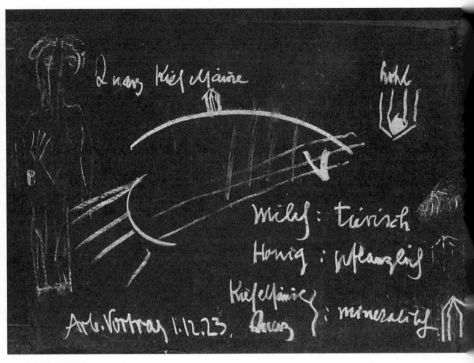

TABLE VI

TABLE VII

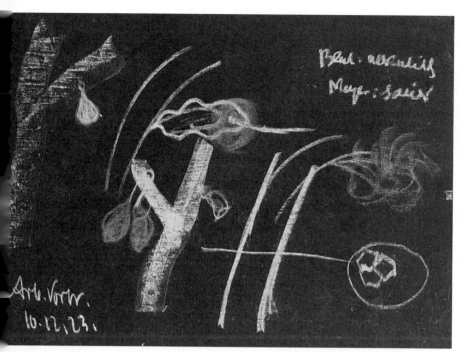

TABLE VIII

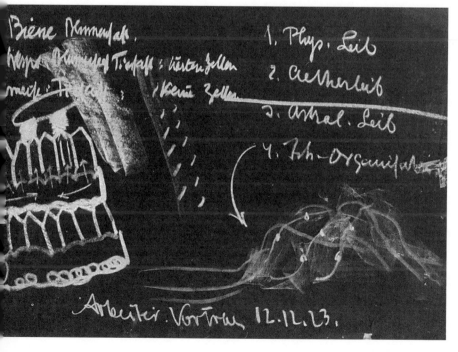

TABLE IX

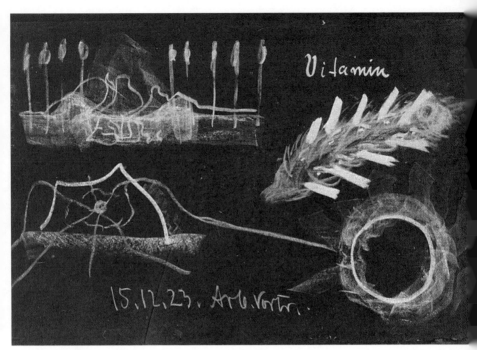

TABLE X

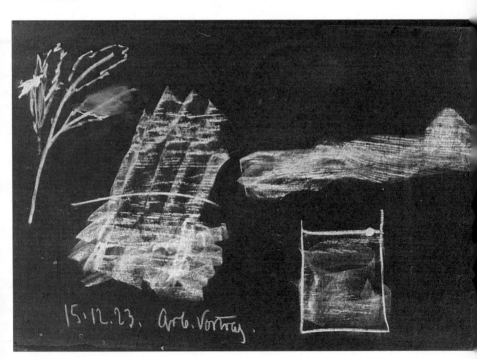

TABLE XI

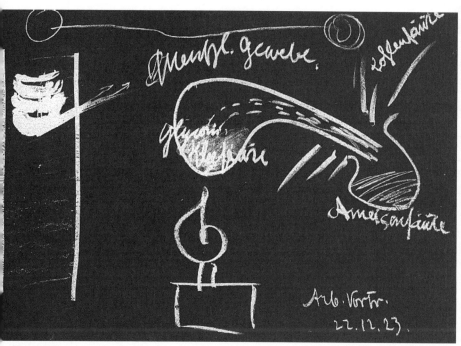

TABLE XII

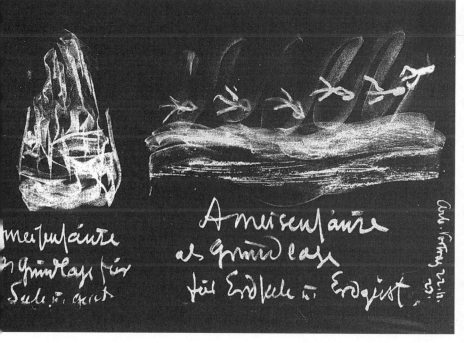

TABLE XIII

• Appendix

Excerpt from a lecture given in Berlin,
September 29, 1905[1]

We have been speaking about the consciousness of the various realms of nature. The organs of the human body also have a consciousness unique to each organ. This type of consciousness manifests itself abnormally in the case of idiots and is an astral consciousness that insects, ants, spiders, etc. also possess. A very different type of consciousness exists in bees. We'll use the bees as an example of how you can arrive at such truths and use them to understand the world around us.

One does not train in matters hidden from ordinary consciousness in the way currently used in schools; it is not directed toward stuffing information into the heads of students. A student does not receive a mass of material that must be learned in a strict manner when learning about hidden spiritual matters, but rather he or she is given a profound statement containing an inner power. That is the way it was done in earlier times. The student had to meditate on this statement while maintaining a complete inner calm. In this way the student would be illumined from within, would experience light within. When human beings arrive at a point

---

1. From "The Basic Elements of Esotericism," GA 93a, 1987. See also *Foundations of Esotericism* (London: Rudolf Steiner Press).

where they are able to see through themselves, they are able to immerse personal consciousness in other beings. For this to happen, one must have taken hold of exactly the point behind the midpoint between the eyes, and must have directed this point of consciousness all the way down into the heart. One will then be able to place one's consciousness into other things; for example, one should then be able to find out what really lives inside an anthill.

You can then also perceive life within a beehive. When you do this, a phenomenon will become apparent, which you will not otherwise observe here on this Earth. Within the activity of a beehive, you will experience something that does not exist anywhere else on this Earth. Whatever may exist on other planets is beyond our current ability to comprehend. For instance, you will not be able to find out what happens on the Sun or on Venus if you cannot apply this method of placing your consciousness into the life and activity of a bee community.

Bees have not fully completed the evolutionary path that we have. In the initial stages of evolution, they were not connected with the same evolutionary chain of events that animals and humans have completed. The consciousness of a beehive, not the individual bees, is of a very high nature. Humankind will not attain the wisdom of such consciousness until the next major evolutionary stage—that of Venus—which will come when the evolution of the Earth stage has finished. Then human beings will possess the consciousness necessary to construct things with a material they create within themselves.

Ants construct an anthill out of various materials, but they still cannot construct cells. The construction of cells is very different at higher levels of existence. There is one thing very different from anything here on Earth, which you learn by immersing yourself into the consciousness of the beehive; by accepting the Venus-consciousness, you can anticipate the one thing that humankind will experience at the Venus level of existence—a complete fading of the sexual element. With bees the sexual element is granted only to one queen. The desire nature of the sexual element is almost completely eliminated; the drones are killed. We see here a prototype of what will be accomplished in future stages of humankind. Work becomes the highest principle. To place your consciousness properly into the beehive, you need to be made suitable for such a task by using the driving force of your own spirit.

Excerpt from a lecture given in Berlin,
June 1, 1908[2]

Last time we boldly advanced into an area where our attention was directed toward certain beings that truly exist as spiritual beings within our real world, but that in a certain way have dropped from the regular course of evolution. Their real significance may be attributed to the fact that they stand apart from ordinary evolution. We're talking about the realm of elemental spiritual beings. We examined these elemental beings, which current educated thinking naturally views as the worst possible kind of superstition, and we discovered that, because of the unique position they hold in the cosmos, they will in the not-too-distant future play a significant role in our own spiritual development.

We have seen how such elemental beings are formed: They are parts of group souls that have been cut off from the primary group soul through an anomaly of the evolutionary process. This cutting off is not a sharp cut, but rather like a ligature that a doctor applies to tie off or strangulate the blood flow to a polyp or tumor; in this case, however, the strangulated part continues to live on its own. By remembering what

2. From "The Influences of Spiritual Entities in the Human Being," GA 102, 1984. See also *The Influence of Spiritual Beings upon Man* (Spring Valley, N.Y.: Anthroposophic Press, 1982).

we determined at the end of the previous lecture, we have been able to bring before our mind's eye the essence of such elemental creatures. We also directed our attention to one of the most recently formed elemental beings. We also indicated how each type of animal, to speak in more general terms, is a sum of all animal beings of a similarly formed type. This sum or collection of similarly formed animals corresponds to a single group soul. We also stated that these group souls play the same role in the astral world as our human soul, if gifted with an I-being, does in the physical world. In reality the human I is a group-self that descended from the astral to the physical plane. In so doing, it has become an individual (nondivisible) I. The animal I-beings still regularly reside on the astral plane and those animals we perceive as individual entities here on the physical plane have only a physical, etheric, and astral body, but their I exists in the astral world in such a way that similarly formed animals are members of a single group I (like the fingers of a hand are part of one body). We also can imagine that what we experience as birth and death in human life does not have the same significance with animals; for when an individual animal dies, the group soul or group I of the animal genus remains alive. You could compare this, if this were possible, to a person who, having lost his hand, possessed the capability of growing back another one. His I would not say: I died because I lost a hand, but it would feel that a member of the body had been renewed. In this way the group I of lions renews a member of its genus when an individual lion dies and is replaced with another. Thus we can understand that birth and death do not have the kind of meaning for the group soul of animals as it does for human beings in the present cycle of development. The group soul of animals is aware of transformations, metamorphoses, the strangulation of its members that are stretched out into the physical world, the loss of these members and their renewal.

We have stated that there are certain forms of animals that go too far in the process of strangulation so that they are no longer able to send back to the astral plane again all that they have brought down to the physical plane. For in the case of a dying animal, what falls away must be absorbed by the world around it. Whereas what the animal infuses with spirit and soul must flow back into the group soul, so that it can then be stretched out anew and grow into a new individual on the physical plane. However, there are certain animal forms that are unable to send everything back again into the group soul, and these left-over things that are torn off, cut off from the group soul then begin to lead an existence on their own as individualized elemental beings. Since our evolution has progressed through various forms and stages and since at each stage such elemental beings were being formed, you can imagine that we have all around us in what we call the surrounding supersensible spiritual world a very large number of types of such elemental beings.

When, for example, an enlightened human being says—"They're talking to us about elemental beings, that they call sylphs or also lemurs; such things do not exist!"—then you would have to give him an answer that sounds a bit strange and paradoxical at the same time: The reason you don't see these things is that you close your mind to the possibility of developing such organs of cognition and perception that would bring you to the point of recognizing these beings. Simply ask the bee, or in other words, the soul of the beehive! It could never close its mind to the existence of sylphs or lemurs, because the elemental beings that are so named come and linger at those special places, specifically, where animal and plant worlds touch—but not all places where this contact takes place, but only where this occurs under certain circumstances. To be sure, when an ox eats grass, there is also such a contact between animal and plant worlds, but this is a very commonplace, regularly occurring event that is situated firmly in the regular progress of evolution. Quite another event in the evolution of our world is the contact between bee and blossom. The reason for this is that in the organization of things they lie further apart and were rejoined subsequently and also because a marvelous energy is developed as the bee touches the blossom, only seen, of course, by someone who has the ability to see into the various spiritual realms. This contact between bee and blossom is one of the most interesting observations that such a spiritual researcher can make, and such an observer will have great difficulty finding the correct expression in our current language for the subtle things like this: he sees the unusual auric envelope or veil that always arises when a bee or similar insect sucks from a blossom. The strange and unusual event the little bee experiences when it sucks from a blossom is not only present in its mouth or in the body of the bee, but rather arises from the interchange of the taste experience of both bee and blossom, an interchange that diffuses around both of them a small etheric aura. Every time the bee sucks, this etheric aura appears, and when this happens in the spiritual world, not observable directly with our normal sense organs, those beings approach and hover near this event because they need something like this. They are attracted by it, because they find, again rather crudely expressed, their "nourishment" there.

On another occasion I stated that we should not even be surprised at the question that someone else might raise: Where do all these beings you are talking about come from? Wherever there is an opportunity for certain beings to exist, they are always there. When a person, by entertaining very evil sentiments, spreads these feelings all around himself or herself, then these sentiments also become alive around this person; and this is exactly what attracts existing beings that only wait for something like this, just as any physical being would wait for nourishment. I once compared this to a clean room without any flies. If all sorts of left-over food sits around in a room, flies appear. This is how it is with spiritual beings: all you have to do is provide the proper nourishment.

A little bee sucking on a blossom spreads about itself a small etheric aura, and this is when such beings appear—especially when and where a swarm of bees, with the sensation of having recently tasted blossoms, lands on a tree and takes off again. The entire swarm of bees becomes enveloped by an etheric aura, but also completely interpenetrated by beings called sylphs and lemurs. Especially in such border areas where various distinctive realms come into contact with each other, these beings are there and they play an important role. They are not only there when this already described fine etheric aura arises, nor are they only interested in satisfying their own hunger; but whereas they are hungry, so to speak, they express this hunger by helping to bring certain animals together with places that will benefit all concerned. They are, in this sense, leaders.

Thus, we see that such beings that have given up their original relationship with the other worlds with which they had been connected and exchanged their former role for a truly remarkable one. They have become beings that serve a good purpose in other worlds. To be sure, when they are used this way, a type of organization exists—they are subordinate to higher beings.

Excerpt from an evening question-and-answer session given in Düsseldorf, April 21, 1909[3]

Question: Is there a difference between the group souls of bees, ants, and corals?

---

3. From "Spiritual Hierarchies and How They Are Reflected in the Physical World," GA 110, 1981. See also *The Spiritual Hierarchies and the Physical World, Reality and Illusion* (Hudson, N.Y.: Anthroposophic Press, 1996).

Certainly; there is a great range of difference. The group soul of a beehive is a very high level being, higher than that of ants. It is of such a high development that you might almost say it is cosmically precocious. It has attained a level of evolutionary development that human beings will later reach in the Venus cycle, which follows the completion of the present Earth cycle. We must view it as we would a precocious child; it stands apart from lines of the normal evolutionary progress that most animals have followed. This is also true of the group soul of ants, except that it is at a lower level. The group soul of corals, however, is on a still higher plane than both. It is higher than, for example, the group soul of cattle. The only problem is that this high level attained by corals is not always suited to nor does it fit easily into the current stage of development—it has anticipated and prematurely developed certain things appropriate to a much more advanced stage of development. But, having done this, it has exposed itself to all sorts of dangers with which it cannot cope. A spiritual zoology is very complicated and the level of development of the various group souls a very wide-ranging one.

Excerpt from a lecture given in Dornach,
November 10, 1923[4]

There is in nature something like a head without a crown, where the same energies are at work outside as well as within the head.... Well, a head that is open in all directions is a beehive. The general activities of bees are actually the same thing we can find within the human head. In the head the activities are, of course, contained within the skull, whereas a beehive is not closed toward exterior activities; at most we give them a

---

4. From "The Human Being as the Harmonization of the Creative Powers of the Logos," GA 230, 1985. See also *Man as Symphony of the Creative Word* (Sussex, U.K.: Rudolf Steiner Press, 1991).

support in the form of a beehive. Thus, we have the same thing inside a beehive influenced by an exterior spiritual influence as we do in the human head, whose spiritual influence is mainly within the head.

Within the beehive there is honey. If we take this honey and enjoy it as an adult, it will give us the same powers that milk does for children, the only difference is that honey provides what the formative powers must give from outside to an older person, whereas the milk provides those powers within the head during childhood.

As children we promote the formative powers through drinking milk; if we need these same powers in adulthood, we must eat honey. You don't really need to eat it in large quantities, since the primary purpose is to derive these specific powers from it.

Comments following Mr. Müller's lecture on bees
Dornach, November 10, 1923

Dr. Steiner: I've just a few comments to make, namely, in regard to the cause of continuous fertility in bees. You may already have noticed from Mr. Müller's comments that there is a problem connected to the artificial breeding of queen bees. It might be interesting to ask Mr. Müller if he thinks this method holds much promise for the future.

Mr. Müller: Yes, I hold this method in high regard for the most part. If you leave the colony to its own devices, and you don't tend it carefully, it might happen that the whole colony will deteriorate. The bad qualities will come through more and more, and whatever was good before is lost.

Dr. Steiner: Since when have bees been bred artificially?

Mr. Müller: For about twelve to fifteen years.

Dr. Steiner: This is the way things stand—I'll talk about this more next time—with the artificial breeding of bees. You can increase their production of honey, all the work they do, and even the worker bee's capability of accomplishing this work. The only problem is, as Mr. Müller has just stated, that this whole procedure should not be carried out in a way that is too rational and businesslike. Next time we'll investigate more thoroughly the matter of breeding of bees, and we'll see that what proves to be an extraordinarily favorable measure upon which something is based today may appear to be good, but that a century from now all breeding of bees would cease if only artificially produced bees were used. We want to be able to see how that which is so wonderfully favorable can change in such a way that it can, in time, gradually destroy whatever was positive in this procedure. And we want to see how, specifically, beekeeping can become of great interest in getting to know all of the secrets of nature, particularly how something, on the one hand, proves to be very fruitful but, on the other hand, simply leads to death and destruction. And so it is that beekeepers can indeed be very happy with all the progress that beekeeping has recently experienced in such a short time, but this happiness will barely continue for one hundred years.

*Two questions answered by Dr. Steiner after the lecture
to the workers on December 10, 1923; reported by R. Hahn*

R. Hahn: I approached Dr. Steiner and asked: What is the cause of foul brood[5] among bees. He said he could give me information about that only after he had thoroughly investigated this disease. But he said that it probably arose from a defective compounding of uric acid by the queen bee. He added: "It is true,

---

5. "Foul brood" refers to a destructive disease of honeybee larvae caused by a bacteria.

isn't it, that a bee has uric acid in its system; probably the faulty creation of uric acid is the cause of this disease."

Regarding the crossbreeding of honeybees from fig wasps mentioned in the same lecture, he answered approximately as follows: "This event took place in old Atlantis, where the individual animal forms were not yet so firmly closed off in their development as they are today. The distinctions between the various types of animals were more fluid and less rigid. Such a crossbreeding would no longer be possible today at this later stage of development."

Excerpt from a lecture given in Dornach,
December 30, 1923[6]

You can immediately see how in certain places in nature the physical powers of Earth join the etheric powers that come from all directions and join it or attach themselves to it. Consider, for example, the proteins found in the physical Earth. As long as they are determined to be made up of sulfur, carbon, oxygen, nitrogen, and hydrogen, they are subordinate to the physical powers on Earth. But once the proteins are lifted into the process of reproduction, they are removed from the physical powers, and the cosmic powers originating from all directions of the heavens begin to influence the proteins that have been split off from their compounds. At this point a new form of protein arises that is a reflection of the entire cosmos.

However, sometimes something else happens. Proteins may be unable to break completely away from the compounds they had originally been a part of, and the process of

---

6. From "World History Viewed Anthroposophically and as the Basis for Understanding the Human Spirit," GA 233, 1980. See also *World History and the Mysteries in the Light of Anthroposophy* (London: Rudolf Steiner Press, 1997).

separation does not go far enough. In order that the process of reproduction may take place in any animal, there might be protein substance present that normally would have to be separated from its compound, so that it could properly be exposed to powers of the entire cosmos and accept its influences. But this animal has been hampered or prevented in some way from providing a protein substance that would conform to or fit the energies and influences of the macrocosm. Protein with the capacity to bring about reproduction must submit appropriately to such macrocosmic influences. The animal is hampered in directly forming, as needed, protein capable of being used in reproduction.

This is the case of the gall wasp. What does it do? It lays its egg into just about any available part of a plant. You can find these galls all over oaks and on other trees where the gall wasp has deposited its eggs. You see these unusual galls on a leaf, and in any of them there may be a gall wasp egg. Why does this happen this way? Why does the gall wasp deposit its egg, let's say, into an oak leaf, so that this gall apple appears where the egg resides—an egg that can now continue to develop? In the open, it would be unable to do so. This happens for the very specific reason—the plant leaf has an etheric body. This is suited for and works harmoniously with the etheric substance of the entire world; and this is what lends support to the gall wasp egg. This egg is unable to help itself, which is why the gall wasp places the egg into a part of a plant where an etheric body is present—one that will harmonize with the entire etheric world. So we can say, the gall wasp comes to the oak to reduce its protein substance compound to a pure protein so that the periphery of the world using a detour through the oak leaf, or oak tree, can provide its beneficial influence for the egg to flourish. Otherwise, the unprotected gall wasp egg would prove unfruitful and die, since the protein cannot be released properly from the compound that holds it tightly together and keeps it from being properly exposed to the life-giving and life-sustaining properties of the etheric world.

You see, there is a possibility of looking into such matters to see how remarkably nature operates. These methods of nature may also be observed elsewhere in nature. Assume, for instance, that an animal is not only incapable of providing the type of embryonic material that the etheric world can work on to bring about reproduction, but this animal also lacks in itself any of the chemicals needed to metabolize and derive nourishment from the foods that travel through its body. You will probably think immediately of the bee as an example.

The bee cannot eat everything; it can eat only what is already prepared for it by a plant. Now look at this very remarkable thing. The bee comes to the flower, seeks the nectar, imbibes it, and converts it to what we so marvel at in a bee—the construction of a honeycomb consisting of many cells. Here we see two strange but very wonderful processes: first, the bee that sits on a flower somewhere outside the hive and collects the nectar; and second, the bee that goes into a beehive and creates from itself, in cooperation with other bees, the wax cells that they will fill with honey. What is happening there? You'll need to look at these cells and determine their form. They are formed so that there is one, then the second attached to it and so on.

They are little cells, the empty chambers of which are formed in such a way as to resemble (though the chambers are filled with a substance and not empty) quartz crystals, silicic acid crystals. If you go into the mountains and look at quartz crystals, you could draw them this way. You'll probably get a slightly irregular drawing, but it will be like the bee cells that are attached to each other. The only difference is that the bee cells are made of wax, and the quartz consists of silica.

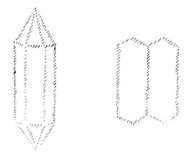

When you investigate the matter further it will be found that the quartz crystal in the mountains was formed with the help of silicic acid at a specific time when our Earth's development was under the general influence of etheric and astral forces. That is when you will see such etheric and astral forces emanating from the area around the Earth and working to help build up the quartz crystals in the silica. You can find them everywhere out in the mountains—those wonderful quartz crystals, six-sided constructions. What you see in those quartz crystals is the same as you will see in the bee cells in the beehive, except that these are empty chambers at first. The bee extracts from the plant the very substance that was once there to help create the hexagonal quartz crystals. The bee extracts this from the flower and within its own body creates replicas of the quartz crystals. What happens between the bee and flower is similar to what once happened out there in the macrocosm.

I mention these things, so that you will see how necessary it is not only to look at the deplorable abstractions in the descriptions of carbon, nitrogen, hydrogen, oxygen, and so on, but that it is very necessary to observe the wonderful creative shaping processes and notice the inner intimate relationships that exist in nature and in natural events.

Excerpt from a lecture given in Dornach,
January 2, 1924 [7]

There are certain events in nature that human beings cause—you can observe them, but their real significance will not be recognized by purely scientific interpretation.

I'll point out to you a very simple phenomenon. In the southern regions there are fig trees. People there have fig trees, which at first produce wild figs, and other trees, the particularly cultivated ones, which produce sweet figs. These people have become very sophisticated in producing them. They cause a certain type of wasp to place its eggs into a fig fruit, one that has grown normally without human intervention. By doing this, the egg produces a maggot that will encapsulate itself. These people, however, interrupt this process so that the young wasp once again lays an egg in the same fig, thus causing two generations of wasps that place their eggs in the same fig fruit during the same year. In this way, they raise the level of sweetness in the fig considerably.

The people of the Mediterranean region do it this way: first they take almost ripened figs and tie two such figs together with bast and hang them on a branch. They allow the wasp to pierce the skin of the figs, which accelerates the ripening of the figs considerably—especially since they were cut off from the branch and then placed on the branch again. This procedure causes the first generation of wasps to develop very quickly and then go to another unpicked fig that will be considerably sweeter because of this procedure.

This process, my friends, is very important, because within nature, and within the substance in figs that continues over time from generation to generation, the same thing happens

7. From "Reflections for Meditation and Indications on How to Deepen One's Understanding of the Healing Art," GA 316, 1988. See also *Course for Young Doctors* (Spring Valley, N.Y.: Mercury Press, 1997).

in a condensed form that happens in a more expanded form when the wasp or, let's say, the honey bee sucks the nectar from the flowers, carries it into the beehive, and manufactures honey. Indeed, the procedure that unfolds before our eyes—beginning with the bee gathering the nectar until the honey is manufactured within the beehive—is the same process that occurs within the fig. By using the wasp to accelerate the ripening of figs—by allowing the young wasp generation to sting them—those Mediterranean people cause a honey-producing process. This fig, stung by the young generation, has begun a honey-making process within itself.

Here you have a metamorphosis of two natural processes; one consists of events separated by time and space—the bees collect nectar from distant flowers, and the honey is made in the beehive from this collected nectar. The other process occurs in the same tree in which the pair of figs is placed. They ripen faster, the new generation of wasps is artificially quickened to reproduce, and the wasps sting another fig on the same tree. Because the other figs are "stung," sweet figs appear everywhere.

Such events would have to be studied properly, since they are the natural processes that come into question here. Within a human being, processes take place that modern physiology and anatomy simply know nothing of. This is because those sciences do not expand their realm of observation to include the kinds of natural processes I have described. It is very important to observe these more subtle processes in nature, for then you will arrive at a true understanding of the human being....

It is important to look at something like a beehive and find out that the individual bee, all by itself, has no intelligence. To be sure, it has instincts, but it is nevertheless stupid. The entire beehive, however, is extraordinarily wise. You see, recently we had some very interesting lecture-discussions with the workers here at the Goetheanum. We had just discussed the realm of bees and someone asked a very interesting question. A beekeeper would understand quite well the importance of this issue: If a beekeeper, who is well liked by a community of bees, should become ill or die, then the entire hive will become disorganized and chaotic. This is in fact true. One of the workers then applied modern scientific logic to this phenomenon and reasoned in this way: We know that the bee does not have very good eyesight; it certainly cannot create within itself any idea or concept of the beekeeper. So how can we consider that there is any sense of a relationship with a particular beekeeper? Furthermore, let's assume that a certain beekeeper has cared for a beehive this year, but then a completely different set of young bees replaces it the next year, except for the queen bee. Where can this sense of belonging together come from—the bees "knowing" their "personal" beekeeper?

I answered that a person who truly knows and understands the human organism also knows that, over given periods, the human organism removes and replaces all substances in the body. Assume that someone becomes familiar with someone who travels to America and comes back after ten years. This person will see someone completely different from the one known ten years earlier. All substances have been exchanged for new ones; a new composition of parts will present itself. It is no different for a beehive; the bees are exchanged for other bees. What remains is the sense of community between beehive and beekeeper. The feeling that they belong to each other is based on the fact that a great wisdom lives in the beehive. It is not simply an assembly of individual bees; the beehive really has its own very specific soul.

From Queen Bee to Social Sculpture

The Artistic Alchemy of Joseph Beuys

• Afterword

SOME READERS will have opened this book out of interest in Rudolf Steiner's biodynamic system of agriculture, hoping to deepen their understanding of the life of bees or of the role beekeeping can play in the organism of a farm or other agricultural venture. Other readers may be concerned to further their understanding of an anthroposophical approach to biology or ecology, specifically to entomology. Still others will be searching these lectures to find how Steiner's treatment of the life of bees and similar social insects relates to other themes of anthroposophy, such as the threefold constitution of the human being and of an ideal social order. But an increasing number of readers will explore these pages with little or no background in Steiner's elaborately comprehensive thought and writings, but with an interest in how these lectures influenced the unique creations of German artist Joseph Beuys (1921–1986). It is primarily to these readers that this introduction is addressed.

From the 1960s through the 1980s the groundbreaking sculptures, drawings, installations, and performance art of Joseph Beuys have frequently been valued as the most significant expression of avant garde art in postwar Europe. In his familiar felt hat and air force ammunition vest, Beuys became a cult figure. Since his death in 1986, the interest of art critics and artists in Beuys's forty years of work has skyrocketed.

Through his own striking but enigmatic artworks as well as his extensive teaching, Beuys influenced two generations of contemporary artists, particularly through his many pupils in Germany. Beyond the art world, Beuys also played a role in European politics, higher education, environmentalism, and social reform.

Beuys is known for his ritualistic "Actions" (performances), his provocative uses of unfamiliar artistic mediums (for example, fat, honey, felt, iron, copper, horns, bones, gelatin, peat, blood, chocolate, conversation), his challenging arrangements of objects and artworks in gallery installations and vitrines, his creative blurring of the boundaries between art and life, his articulate theoretical statements on art and social reform, and his intense, wiry drawings. These creations have fascinated and intrigued, but also largely puzzled, the international art world for more than three decades. Although Beuys adapted for his work aspects of the 1960s and 1970s avant garde movements known as process, performance, installation, and conceptual art, he used them in personal and unusual ways to shape creations whose meanings remain elusive.

Disenchanted with the elitism of what he called the "art world ghetto," Beuys saw the end of modernism in art as a transition to an expanded "social art" or "social sculpture" in which *everyone* could be creative and participate democratically to resculpt the body social. Beuys's "totalized concept of art" referred to the elemental process of human form-making, whether this occurred in artworks, thoughts, speech, or social interaction. Beuys's importance lies not only in his impressively original and influential artworks, but also in his unique and sometimes controversial efforts to bridge the gap between art and contemporary life, without sacrificing the integrity of either.

What has not generally been realized in existing critical writings is how completely Beuys's work was imbued with

Rudolf Steiner's anthroposophy. While Beuys sometimes mentioned Steiner more or less in passing, apparently no art critic or historian has yet realized the tremendous extent of Beuys's reliance on Steiner's ideas nor appreciated Beuys's originality in adapting Steiner's often complex and unfamiliar ideas to his own artwork within a radically shifting context of contemporary art that was quite different from Steiner's own artistic productions. In many cases anthroposophical ideas provide the keys that unlock Beuys's real intentions for particular artistic projects—and no anthroposophical content played a greater role in Beuys's formative development than these nine lectures on bees.

Beuys made one of his clearest acknowledgments of Steiner's influence in a 1971 letter that referred to "Rudolf Steiner, about whom I had to think over and over again since my childhood. I know that he has left me the mission to sweep away gradually, *in my own way*, the alienation and distrust people have toward the supersensible."[1] While a soldier, having been drafted in 1941 at age twenty, Beuys first studied some of Steiner's books with his childhood friend Fritz Rolf Rothenburg, who died in the Sachsenhausen concentration camp in 1943. While he was not particularly enthusiastic about the books then, after the war, as a student at the Art Academy in Düsseldorf in 1947, he again took up Steiner's writings and found them more profound and important.

Beuys was part of a group of seven students from Ewald Mataré's sculpture class who were interested in anthroposophy. They made contact with Max Benirschke, a former pupil of Steiner and a leader of anthroposophical activity in

---

1. Joseph Beuys, trans., Marion Briggs with Martin Barkhoff and Elaine Busby, *Joseph Beuys: His Art and Rudolf Steiner*, ed., Marion Briggs (West Hoathly, Art Section: 1995), p. 21; translated from its original publication in *Gerd Hatje*, ed., *Joseph Beuys—Plastische Bilder*, 1947–1970 (Stuttgart: 1990).

Düsseldorf. Over two years Beuys regularly attended anthroposophical lectures, seminars, and a weekly study group led by Benirschke. For a few years after this Beuys regularly visited a forest cottage at Weissenseifen that belonged to his former student friend Günther Mancke. Benirschke also made summer visits there, sometimes leading marathon sessions of reading unpublished Steiner lectures from his collection. In August 1951 Beuys traveled with a group of Weissenseifen friends to Dornach, Switzerland, where he was impressed by performances of Steiner's mystery plays, an exhibition of Steiner's sketches for the ceiling paintings and engraved glass windows of his Goetheanum building, and discussions on architectural design with Goetheanum architectural collaborator Hermann Rantzenberger. He was somewhat less impressed by many of the anthroposophists he met.

Although Beuys did eventually join the Anthroposophical Society in 1973, he always held back somewhat from association with orthodox anthroposophy, apparently for two reasons. The first was his disappointment with what he perceived in many anthroposophists as a something less than genuine attitude and an inconsistent thinking. The second was his constitutional inability to take up what he saw as a repetitive, clichéd anthroposophical visual art practice. He was unable to recognize the personal possibility for an independent creativity in what he once referred to as "the Anthroposophical Museum." Yet he did on occasion support Steiner's ideas about art, and he said that others should take up the anthroposophical artistic practice based directly on Steiner's visual art, which he felt unable or unwilling to pursue.[2]

---

2. See, for example, ibid., p. 11–16 and 21; *Joseph Beuys im Gespräch mit Knut Fischer und Walter Smerling* (Cologne: Kiepenheuer & Witsch, *Kunst Heute Nr. 1*, 1989), p. 52; and Carin Kuoni, ed., *Energy Plan for the Western Man: Joseph Beuys in America* (New York: Four Walls Eight Windows, 1990), pp. 256–258.

Beuys soon linked up with others working on Steiner's idea of a threefold social organism and made the promotion of these ideas a central part of his activity from the mid-1960s onward. He also incorporated into his work fundamental anthroposophical ideas about the human constitution, cosmic and human evolution, and higher forms of pure thinking, although he didn't directly acknowledge Steiner as the source of most of these ideas. Beuys once told author Volker Harlan about his own, independent supersensible experiences and perceptions, the capacity for which he acquired from reading Steiner's works, and how he had found that Steiner's explanations were able to explain adequately what he had experienced.[3]

At his death Beuys's library included more than 120 volumes by Steiner, thirty-some of which were extensively marked with underlining and marginal drawings.[4] As his own original contribution, Beuys cited his "totalized," "anthropological" understanding of art—the ideas that everyone is an artist; that one can be a form-creating artist even in thinking and speaking; that art expanded to life as "social sculpture" is needed in our time; and that this creative intelligence of the people, this enlarged art, is the real capital of an economy.

Yet even here Steiner's ideas may have influenced Beuys more than Beuys consciously realized or recalled. Consider the following quotations from Steiner: "I wanted to show that the realm otherwise dealt with only by the artist in imagination must now become the serious concern of the human race, for the reason that it represents the stage humanity

---

3. Volker Harlan, *Was Ist Kunst? Werkstattgespräch mit Beuys* (Stuttgart: Urachhaus, 1986), pp. 87–88.
4. A list of these books is given in Volker Harlan, Dieter Koepplin, and Rudolf Velhagen, eds., *Joseph Beuys—Tagung Basel 1–4. Mai 1991* (Basel: Wiese Verlag, 1991), pp. 292–295.

must reach to lay hold upon the supersensible, which the brain is incapable of grasping." "Genuine art ... is an affair of the people; genuine art is essentially social in character." "A real permeation by social art of our community through [artistic] education would give us a true culture of the will." "What we must learn to do is to bring art into our thinking...." "All real philosophers have been artists in the realm of concepts." "The outer expression of intelligence, in this connection, is in the manifold formations of capital." "... intelligence works in capital as inventiveness in connection with the whole social life." Although Steiner may not always have intended precisely the same meaning as Beuys, nonetheless the similarities are striking and must have been highly suggestive to Beuys.[5]

. . . .

Bees and Beuys—this must be a discussion on the threshold between art and nature, rich with associations, unexpected transformations, and veiled meanings. Beuys had apparently maintained an interest in bees for some years. A student friend tells of his composting sulphured bees, and Beuys himself related how he would regularly leave his studio doors open when warming beeswax so that his studio sometimes

---

5. In consecutive order, the sources of these Steiner quotations are as follows: Quoted in Otto Palmer, *Rudolf Steiner on His Book The Philosophy of Freedom*, trans., Marjorie Spock (Spring Valley, New York: Anthroposophic Press, 1975), p. 39 [alternate trans., *Some Characteristics of Today*, trans., unknown (London: Rudolf Steiner Press, 1943), p. 18]; *A Social Basis for Education*, trans., unknown (Forest Row: Steiner Schools Fellowship, 1958/1994), p. 44; ibid., p. 46; *Speech and Drama*, trans., Mary Adams (London: Anthroposophical Publishing Company, 1960), p. 325; *The Philosophy of Spiritual Activity: A Philosophy of Freedom*, trans., Rita Stebbing (London: Rudolf Steiner Press, 1992 [1894]), p. 177; *Economics: The World as One Economy*, trans., Owen Barfield and T. Gordon-Jones, rev., Christopher Houghton Budd (Canterbury: New Economy Publications, 1993), p. 48; and ibid., p. 73.

filled with "millions" of visiting bees.[6] It required someone with Beuys's unique combination of interest and knowledge in nature, art, spirituality, and anthroposophy to see the potential in Steiner's surprising lectures on bees for a radically new approach to visual art. Such an encounter also had to occur at a point in Beuys's life when he was searching and listening intensely for signs of a new direction for both his artwork and his life work.

Since his childhood, Beuys had been an eager student of the natural world. During his youth in the Lower Rhine village of Kleve, he showed a keen interest, both scientific and romantic, in nature, assembling and displaying collections of specimens, and later as a teenager desiring to study natural science. During his military training as a radio operator in 1940–1941, Beuys attended zoology classes at the Reich University of Posen. This was made possible by his military instructor, Heinz Sielmann, a former student of biology and maker of nature films. Sielmann and Beuys collaborated for a number of years after the war, particularly on making Sielmann's nature films. Beuys, however, quickly became disillusioned with the narrow specialization of interest characteristic of university science, and after the war he turned to a career in art (nonetheless, maintaining a small scientific laboratory in a corner of his studio well into the 1950s).

Whereas Beuys's early sculptural work was consciously formed within a modernized version of the stylized Romanesque tradition of art, frequently with a Christian content such as crucifixions or pietàs, he gradually was able to free himself from this more traditional approach. After a personal

---

6. Briggs, ed., *Joseph Beuys*, p. 9; and Robert Conybeare, "Interview with Joseph Beuys," part of Dip. A. D. thesis, Faculty of Art, Wolverhampton Polytechnic, 1971.

crisis in the mid-1950s Beuys emerged with a hunger for a more radical approach to art. Outwardly, he began participating in the interdisciplinary art performances of the international Fluxus movement in the early 1960s. Yet inwardly he had already been struggling with new artistic conceptions that he partially derived from such anthroposophical sources as Steiner's *Bees*. While he supported the Fluxus goal of abolishing the distinction between artistic and non-artistic practices of creativity, he criticized their anti-individualism and lack of an epistemological theory with a clearly defined social goal. In Steiner's work Beuys found both a suitably holistic epistemology and clearly articulated social and spiritual ideals.

Beuys once commented that his earliest work, such as his drawings of the late 1940s and early 1950s, often had been spiritually esoteric in content but not yet in form.[7] He wanted to create art that would reach viewers at more inward levels of experience. Rather than appeal to a conceptual, verbal dialogue about his art, Beuys tried to establish an "energy dialogue." Much of his work attempted to convey forces and energies of the natural and human worlds, often grasped at a pre-linguistic level. "All my actions are based upon concepts of basic human energies in the form of images," he remarked.[8]

Beuys saw the animal kingdom as an ally for the evolutionary process of broadening and deepening human awareness. Not only the bee, but also the horse, stag, elk, coyote, fox, swan, goat, hare, moose, and wasp appeared in his drawings, performances, and sculptures. Beuys felt that the essential, higher being of animals gave access to forgotten spiritual energies now needed again by human society, especially

---

7. See Harlan, *Was Ist Kunst?*, p. 86.
8. Götz Adriani, Winfried Konnertz, & Karin Thomas, *Joseph Beuys: Life and Works*, trans., Patricia Lech (Woodbury, N.Y.: Barron's Educational Series, 1979), p. 257.

when apprehended on a purely perceptual level without pre-determined concepts. "Why do I work with animals to express invisible powers?" he asked rhetorically in 1974. "You can make these energies very clear if you enter another kingdom that people have forgotten, and where vast powers survive as big personalities."[9] "I think the crux of the matter," he related in 1969, "is that my work is permeated with thoughts that do not originate in the official development of art but in scientific concepts.... I tried to do something new for both science and art. I wanted to widen both areas."[10]

It is just in this area that Steiner's lectures on bees suggested rich possibilities to Beuys. One need only consider Steiner's enunciation in the first lecture that nothing that "exists somewhere in nature is without certain powers." Not only would Steiner's characterizations of the intimate ecological relationships active in the "household of nature" have appealed to Beuys, but Steiner repeatedly emphasized that we must learn to recognize the spiritual processes at work in nature and that these can provide significant pictures for human life as well. "Looking at things in a properly natural way," he said in the ninth lecture, "we can see in all the processes of nature, symbols and representations of those things that occur in human life." As examples, Steiner spoke of the relationship between the beehive and the human head and body, between the selfless wisdom living in the bee colony and future human social life, between a swarm of bees leaving and returning to the hive and human reincarnation, and between the "hexagonally-acting powers" expressed in the structure of the beehive (and quartz crystals) and those active in the building processes of human blood, muscles, and bone.

---

9. Kuoni, ed., *Energy Plan*, p. 142.
10. Ibid., p. 90.

Yet Beuys was not only seeking more spiritually or symbol-ically meaningful pictures for his art. In fact, he contrasted the merely "retinal" kind of seeing typical today in both visual art and ordinary life with the ability to apprehend a more complete "force constellation in the field of vision," including, for example, the warmth dimension of colors and the spiritual or even sacramental processes active in material substances.[11] In this connection, Steiner's bee lec-tures probably suggested to Beuys new approaches to visual art based more on the invisible qualities of substances them-selves than on their elements of form or content within a specific artwork. In the third lecture Steiner also contrasted merely visual experience with effects from warmth, taste, smell, and chemical changes. He also discussed the spiri-tual, nearly magical influences that are carried in nature by such substances as honey, bee poison, oxalic acid, and for-mic acid. He emphasized the spiritual *activity* invisibly at work behind the outwardly perceived substance.

Beuys began to shape his artworks out of the anthropo-sophical understanding of the spiritual qualities or activities of substances, plants, and animals in nature—not as symbols of these activities but as direct manifestations of them com-posed into meaningful signs. Beuys's art questioned the belief that we can adequately understand the inner workings of our world through normal modes of perception. He was clear that organs of knowing that are quite different from ordinary logical, analytical thinking must be employed to apprehend the forces at work in material substances, capaci-ties of *Imagination, Inspiration,* and *Intuition* that he had learned about from Steiner's work.[12]

---

11. See Harlan, *Was Ist Kunst?* pp. 21 and 23.
12. Ibid., p. 66.

Based on his reading of Steiner, Beuys sought an understanding of the creation of visual form related to the anthroposophical description of the three fundamental human
psychological ("soul") activities of thinking, feeling, and willing. Or, to indicate a related theme in Steiner, we could say
that Beuys looked for a way to apply "mediated polarity" to
visual form—that is, two opposite, polar tendencies with a central, mediating element between them. His "Theory of Sculpture," which was worked out during the 1950s, largely in
connection with his fundamental bronze and iron relief sculpture *SåFG SåUG (Sunrise-Sunset)* begun in 1953 but first exhibited in 1964, was based on a fundamental complex of
polarities: "The theory is based on the passage from chaotic
material to ordered form through sculptural movement:

chaos		order
undetermined		determined
organic	movement	crystalline
warm		cold
expansion		contraction

... Really it is the same element repeated in the two different
states of *contraction* and *expansion*, principles essential to sculpture."[13] As Martin Barkhoff has pointed out, the title of this
relief sculpture readily recalls the two pairs of sunrise-sunset
pastel sketches given by Steiner as exercises for the training of
painters.[14] Watercolor painting workshops on these and other

---

13. Caroline Tisdale, *Joseph Beuys* (New York: Thames and Hudson, 1979), p. 44.
14. See Marie Groddeck, *The Seven Training Sketches for the Painter by Rudolf Steiner*,
trans., Inge Martin (London: Michael Press, 1978); Hilde Boos-Hamburger, *The
Nine Training Sketches for the Painter (Nature's Moods) by Rudolf Steiner* (London: Rudolf Steiner Press, 1982); Anon., *Rudolf Steiners Malerischer Impuls* (Dornach, Switzerland: Philosophisch-Anthroposophischer Verlag am Goetheanum, 1971; and
Elisabeth Koch and Gerard Wagner, *The Individuality of Colour*, trans., Peter Stebbing (London: Rudolf Steiner Press, 1980).

polarically paired sketches by Steiner were offered to visitors at the Goetheanum conference Beuys attended in 1951.[15] The reference to contraction and expansion points to the scientific work of Goethe, especially his *The Metamorphosis of Plants*, which Steiner had clarified and interpreted in several early writings that Beuys had read.[16]

Beuys's theory of sculpture was one expression of his wish to develop an approach to visual art based upon the fundamental processes underlying the formation of matter and form in the world that appears to our senses. His next task was to find substances that could be used to express the principles of this theory as directly as possible. His *SåFG SåUG* sculpture had combined bronze and iron because of the expressive polarity of copper and iron, two materials he often used together thereafter. For a number of reasons—many of which Beuys could have learned about through anthroposophy—copper represented a flexible, more feminine quality characterized by ready conductivity of heat and electricity, high resonance and luster, and an enlivening affect on fluids. Among metals, iron represented the opposite pole, with its hard, masculine, earth-bound nature. Both the ancients and Steiner associated copper with Venus and iron with Mars.[17]

Beuys, however, looked for a single substance that could express directly both the polar extremes and the artistic movement between them. Because he felt the institutions

15. See Briggs, ed. *Joseph Beuys*, p. 14.
16. See in particular Steiner's *Goethean Science*, trans., William Lindeman (Spring Valley, New York: Mercury Press, 1988).
17. In addition to numerous scattered references on the relationships of metals to both the planetary macrocosm and the human microcosm in Steiner's lectures, it is likely that Beuys would have been familiar with one or both of two anthroposophical secondary works on the metals: Rudolf Hauschka, *The Nature of Substance*, trans., Marjorie Spock and Mary T. Richards (London: Rudolf Steiner Press, 1983); and Wilhelm Pelikan, *The Secrets of Metals*, trans., Charlotte Lebensart (Spring Valley: Anthroposophic Press, 1973.

and mentality of modern society tended too far toward the cold, ordered, determined pole of this theory, he wanted to emphasize the opposite pole in his artwork. In particular, he spoke of developing "warmth sculptures," and he looked for materials that were sensitive to warmth. We should recall here Steiner's description of warmth as the border state between the material and spiritual worlds, the closest to the physical world of four types of supersensible "etheric life forces" (and distinguishable from the purely material "heat"). Beuys also was attracted to warmth as a fundamental characteristic of the human being, particularly the warmth of will and feeling he felt was needed to balance the coldness of the rational intellect that had become so one-sidedly dominant in western civilization. Underlying this interest was also Steiner's depiction of the warmth carried in our blood circulation as the physical basis for the human I itself.

Beuys began using beeswax as an artistic material in the 1950s. He used it to demonstrate his theory of sculpture because it could easily be melted into an amorphous liquid state by warmth—or as a candle become a source of light and warmth—yet could also be cooled and hardened into definite forms, such as the crystallized geometry of the honeycomb.[18] He was further attracted to beeswax as a medium because it was produced by the bees "in an environment that has a certain organic warmth." Beuys described these warmth processes of the bees: "The quality of warmth is there in honey, but also in wax, and also in pollen and nectar, because the bee consumes from the plant the thing that has the greatest possible quality of warmth. An alchemical process is going on somewhere in the flower, where the actual warmth process primarily develops, where fragrances are created, which disperse, and where nectar forms, which is really the plant's own

---

18. See Adriani, Konnertz, and Thomas, *Joseph Beuys*, p. 41.

honey."[19] As Steiner describes in the second lecture of this book, the process of melting and solidifying beeswax closely reflects what happens with a kind of wax in our own bodies and our blood circulation, and Beuys's theory of sculpture is ultimately a theory of human consciousness and creativity.

Aside from some more or less unformed beeswax artworks (such as *Wax Sculpture* of 1953), Beuys created three "queen bee" sculptures in 1947 and 1952 out of beeswax on a wooden base. The first two included small female figures as a sign for feminine spiritual fertility, creativity, and openness to the future: "To express spiritual power and potential I tend to use the female figure," Beuys explained about this recurring theme in his work.[20] As Steiner pointed out, only the queen bee develops in a rounded, sack-shaped cell rather than the regular hexagonal cells of the beehive, thus representing something of the warmer, less crystallized pole of the two extremes in Beuys's sculpture theory. Only *Queen Bee III* very closely resembled a bee, but even she was an image relating more to human, and even divine, potentials. Beuys also executed a number of queen bee drawings during the 1950s. "These 'Queen Bees' all possess something that is very strongly organic," he related. "In the middle is a sort of heart point, from which the forms radiate and then encircle again. Actually it is a totally organic picture, including

19. Quoted from an interview with Beuys printed in the December 1975 *Rheinische Bienenzeitung*, the oldest German beekeeping journal, in *Stachelhaus, Joseph Beuys*, p. 57. See also Adriani, Konnertz & Thomas, *Joseph Beuys*, pp. 39–41. Beuys was disappointed that most beekeepers he met no longer had much feeling for the warmth generated within the beehive; see Harlan, *Was Ist Kunst?*, p. 22.

20. Tisdale, *Joseph Beuys*, p. 50. This also closely followed Steiner's characterization of women as tending to be more readily open to spiritual matters than men. Beuys related the contrasting, one-sided masculine element to aggression and to over-intellectualized concentration on cold and abstract powers of the head.

things that represent Christianity, heart, love, and resignation. I attempted to portray this as directly organic, as a sort of psychological process. In this light the 'Queen Bees' are nothing more than moving crosses."[21] Beuys also depicted his Queen Bees as symbols of the love that surrenders itself for others, where the queen's beating wings can appear like an animated cross moving around its heart center.[22] This recalls Steiner's emphasis in the first lecture on the relationship of the beehive to love, but it also points to another anthroposophical element in Beuys's artwork.

Early in his artistic career Beuys created a number of sculpted crosses and crucifixes, usually in bronze, and throughout his career the sign of the cross was a key element in his work. On the one hand, Beuys related the cross to the materialized, four-square, space-time coordinate consciousness of the modern scientific world view (also mentioning the crosshair used in gun sights for more accurate killing). On the other hand, he identified the cross, or at least the rose cross, with an expanded understanding of Christ.[23] Looking back on his early career, he commented, "It became clear to me that what is Christian is not reached through depictions of the figure of Christ." "The Christian element is ... connected with the powers of nature, with the planetary movements, with cosmic dimensions." Following Steiner's revelations, Beuys identified the resurrected Christ in modern times as "a divine human energy" continually present in the natural world and in the higher ego of the human being, as seen with the "inner eye," "a highly developed form of human possibilities, especially in relation to

21. Ibid., p. 44.

22. Friedhelm Mennekes, *Beuys on Christ: A Position in Dialogue* (Stuttgart: Verlag Katholisches Bibelwerk, 1989), pp. 99–100.

23. See Adriani, Konnertz & Thomas, *Joseph Beuys*, pp. 47–48.

his future development."[24] Beuys could also relate this understanding to his work with substances and art as a universal creativity, referring to "the etheric element of the substance, which is generated through Christ himself and through Man himself who is probably in the position to perform what is called creativity."[25] Beuys felt that an adequate artistic representation of Christ in the twentieth century could only be made through movement, referring to his own Actions.[26]

Beuys's earliest crosses incorporated an element of movement, irregular organic shapes, and modernized versions of the traditional Celtic-Irish "resurrection, or sun cross," uniting the living sun disk with the symbol of death and thereby connecting Christ with the sun energies of nature. It was only a small step to progress to the queen bee as the female sign of the Christ energy and love within the natural world. Steiner associated Christ with the sun and in the seventh lecture portrayed bees as "creatures of the sun" with the queen bee having a special relationship to sun forces.[27] This was a stage in Beuys's efforts to free himself from the traditional religious imagery of his Catholic upbringing so that he could develop more adventurous forms of artistic expression.

Ultimately, beeswax proved less suitable than fat as an indicator medium for Beuys's theory of sculpture. The source of his use of fat is often attributed by writers to Beuys's wartime plane crash in the Crimea in 1943. He was rescued and nursed back to health by nomadic Tartars, who salved his

---

24. Ibid, pp. 31 and 130.
25. Ibid., p. 49.
26. Mennekes, *Beuys on Christ*, pp. 17 and 57–59.
27. For example, see Rudolf Steiner, *Cosmosophy*, vol. 1, trans., Alice Wulsin (Spring Valley, New York: Anthroposophic Press, 1985), pp. 175–176; or *The Bridge between Universal Spirituality and the Physical Constitution of Man*, trans., Dorothy S. Osmond (Spring Valley, New York: Anthroposophic Press, 1958), pp. 42–46.

many wounds with animal fat while he lay mostly unconscious for eight days. While one cannot ignore the role of such a key life experience, Beuys himself discounted its importance for his use of fat, and instead pointed to the material's aptness for his Theory of Sculpture. Beuys found that this new material reacted more sensitively to warmth than did beeswax. When he exhibited his famous *Fat Chair* of 1963 and innumerable fat corners and fat elements in sculptures, Actions, and installations, he also found that it was a more provocatively expressive material that strongly affected viewers and could lead to opportunities for extended dialogues on the ideas behind his artworks. Nearly all of Beuys's seventy-some Actions were followed by group conversations on their meanings, and it became one of Beuys's goals to approach such conversations as steps toward building the social organism itself as a work of art.

For Beuys, the other artistic material inspired by Steiner's bee lectures was honey. Honey not only carried the same warmth character as beeswax, but added other references important for Beuys's larger artistic mission. Honey had been considered a sacred substance by the ancients. The Indians, Egyptians, and Greeks all used it in rituals connected with the transitions between the material and spiritual worlds, with birth and death. In Norse and Greek mythology honey was the food of the gods. Beuys himself pointed out many of these associations:

> Honey as such also used to be seen in a mythological context as a spiritual substance, so of course the bee was divine. There is the Apis cult. The Apis cult is a very widespread culture, basically a culture of Venus that concerned itself especially with bees. What mattered was not having honey to eat; it was the whole process that was regarded as important, a link between cosmic and

earthly forces that absorbed it all.... Basically, my sculptures, too, are a kind of Apis cult.[28]

Of course, Beuys had read in these lectures by Steiner about
the ancient Venus cult associated with the beehive, the
upbuilding and healing "formative forces of the hexagonal
principle" in honey, and the strong relationships among
honey, the beehive, and the human being.[29]

Beuys used honey prominently in two of his most well-
known artworks. The first was his three-hour 1965 gallery
Action for the opening of his art exhibition at Galerie
Schmela in Düsseldorf, *How to Explain Pictures to a Dead Hare.*[30]
In this strange but curiously compelling performance, Beuys
sat on a stool or walked about inside the closed gallery gestur-
ing as he silently explained his artworks to a dead hare he cra-
dled in his arm or let touch the pictures with its paw. Viewers
could watch through an open doorway or a street-side window.
There they saw Beuys with his head covered in honey and gold
leaf speaking to the hare. A felt sole was tied to his left shoe, an
identical sole, except that it was made of iron, was tied to his
right shoe, a leg of the stool was wrapped in felt, and under
the stool was a "radio" constructed of modern electronic parts
and animal bones connected to an amplifier. The felt was
made of hare's fur and carried a warming, insulating effect. In
accordance with Steiner's ideas, it was appropriate that the felt

28. Quoted in Stachelhaus, *Joseph Beuys*, p. 58.

29. This would include Steiner's related comments in *Man as Symphony of the
Creative Word*, trans., Judith Compton-Burnett (London: Rudolf Steiner
Press, 1970), pp. 202–203 (also read by Beuys and partially quoted in the appendix excerpt in this book from November 10, 1923) and Steiner's hint in
the fourth lecture about the relationship between the hexagonal beehive
cells and quartz crystals with the hemoglobin of human blood, which also has
a hexagonal chemical structure.

30. As Beuys sometimes explained, an Action was just "a sculpture dissected out
into its essential elements." (Kuoni, ed., *Energy Plan*, p. 142).

sole was attached to the more inner, receptive left side of Beuys's body, while the sole made of hard, masculine iron was attached to the more active, outwardly-oriented right side.

The Action raised questions about the possibilities of adequately explaining art or the world, and about what capacities would be needed for real understanding. Beuys commented: "Using honey on my head I am naturally doing something that is concerned with thought. The human capacity is not to give honey, but to think—to give ideas. In this way the deathlike character of thought is made living again. Honey is doubtlessly a living substance. Human thought can also be living."[31] Gold is the metal of the sun, and Beuys was also indicating the potential for bringing a sun-like quality into thinking, a Christ-related theme that Steiner also spoke about.[32] The hare, which literally digs into matter, represented the sharpened materialistic thinking of modern science that now needed to be filled by living, intuitive thinking. The fact that the hare was dead, recalls the repeated anthroposophical image of the deathly qualities of modern, abstract thought. Beuys spoke to an externalized part of himself (representative of all human beings), re-enlivening and reintegrating the dead thing that now existed outside himself as "object." At the same time, the hare represented a still authentic spiritual power alive in the animal world that human beings have largely forgotten. In 1962 Beuys had executed in hare's blood a drawing titled *Head*, an earlier artistic attempt to create a sign for bringing a living substance (blood) to materialistically hardened thought. Beuys explained that "everyone consciously or unconsciously recognizes the problem of explaining things, particularly

---

31. Adriani, Konnertz & Thomas, *Joseph Beuys*, p. 132.
32. Rudolf Steiner, *Karmic Relationships: Esoteric Studies*, vol. 6, trans., D.S.O. and E.H.G. (London: Rudolf Steiner Press, 1971), pp. 13–15.

where art and creative work are concerned, or anything that involves a certain mystery or questioning. The idea of explaining to an animal conveys a sense of the secrecy of the world and of existence that appeals to the imagination.... Even a dead animal preserves more powers of intuition than some human beings with their stubborn rationality.... Imagination, inspiration, intuition, and longing all lead people to sense that these other levels also play a part in understanding."[33]

A later Beuys project that involved honey was his *Honey Pump at the Workplace* installation in 1977 at the large international art show "Documenta 6" in Kassel. This installation ran for the hundred days of the exhibition (June 24 to October 2) and was presented as part of the introduction of another Beuys initiative—the establishment of the Free International University for Creativity and Interdisciplinary Research. For this project, two ship's engines, 220 pounds of fat (margarine), and a steel container holding two tons of honey were installed in the stairwell of the Museum Fridericianum and linked through clear plastic tubing to the large curved space where a busy program of discussions, seminars, lectures, films, and demonstrations of the Free International University took place throughout the one hundred days. During these events the honey was pumped through a network of tubing that circulated above the hall. Beuys explained his basic idea as follows:

> With *Honey Pump* I am expressing the principle of the Free International University working in the bloodstream of society. Flowing in and out of the heart organ—the steel honey container—are the main arteries through which the honey is pumped out of the engine room with a pulsing sound, circulates round the Free University area, and returns to the heart. The whole thing is only complete

---

33. Tisdale, *Joseph Beuys*, p. 105.

with people in the space round which the honey artery flows and where the bee's head is to be found in the coiled loops of tubing with its two iron feelers.[34]

By associating the warmth quality of the natural substance honey with the warm nature of the blood, Beuys suggested that warmth of feeling and will, as well as alert and self-present minds, were necessary for successful Free University discussions.

In this installation Beuys was concerned with having elements that represent the three psychological elements of the human being, often described by Steiner in relation to their physiological bases: thinking with the nerve-sense system (head); feeling with the rhythmic system (chest); and willing with the metabolic-limb system (abdomen and limbs).[35] In *Honey Pump* Beuys represented the head by a long pipe that rose from the stairwell "engine room" up to the skylight roof of the hall and then curved back around toward the ground, as a version of the shepherd's crook, or "Eurasian staff," he had often used in other performances and installations.[36]

---

34. Ibid., p. 254.

35. Steiner first announced these relationships in his 1917 book *Riddles of the Soul*, trans., William Lindeman (Spring Valley, New York: Mercury Press, 1996), pp. 131–140; see also an earlier, partial translation by Owen Barfield, *The Case for Anthroposophy* (London: Rudolf Steiner Press, 1970). Steiner elaborated and applied these relationships in many later lectures, perhaps most notably in his 1919 lectures *The Foundations of Human Experience*, trans., Robert F. Lathe and Nancy Parsons Whittaker (Hudson, NY: Anthroposophic Press, 1996).

36. An additional meaning is carried by the Eurasian staff here, again derived from Steiner's various lectures on human evolution in relationship to eastern and western thinking and spirituality. Beuys once explained that the staff represented the historical developmental path of humanity from earlier civilizations of the East to the more modern civilizations of the West, reaching, with the beginning in our time, a kind of knot or curve relating to a turn back again toward the qualities of the East. "Today…," Beuys commented, "I think there is a possibility that the direction of the development may change and that light will come from the West, provided that man develops in a state of full awareness, as I imagine he will" (Kuoni, ed., *Energy Plan*, pp. 156–157).

> At one place the honey was fixed. Therefore, I had the impression that there must thus be something like a brain, like a head, where something above damming up the head function takes over, above in the roof of the Documenta.[37]

The honey circulation system with its steel container "heart" represented the human circulation system and related life of feeling—even as Steiner describes an analogy between bees and blood cells or blood circulation in the second lecture on bees. Finally, there was the 220 pounds of fat placed into continual motion by "two motors, which I had coupled with a large copper cylinder, which continuously moved the fat at high speed; and that was for me the representative of the will,..."[38] Of course, this trinity also represented Beuys's Theory of Sculpture, with the "head" as the form pole, the will as the "chaotic" pole, and feeling as the movement element of circulation between these two. Following Steiner, this psychosomatic three-foldness also was echoed at the spiritual level in three small, empty bronze pots that Beuys had "doubly cleaned" and placed in a corner in the "engine room" as a sign for those higher spiritual sources of thinking, feeling, and willing that Steiner called Imagination, Inspiration, and Intuition.[39]

The Free International University program at Documenta 6 dealt with a range of contemporary social themes and issues where radical and creative new thinking was needed to overcome existing problems, including human rights, urban decay, nuclear energy, migrancy, the Third World, violence, Northern Ireland, manipulation by mass communications media, and unemployment. These topics were discussed in

---

37. Harlan, *Joseph Beuys*, p. 55 (my translation).
38. Ibid. (my translation).
39. See *Riddles of the Soul*, pp. 140–143; see also ibid., p. 61.

an interdisciplinary way by a changing stream of international politicians, lawyers, economists, trade unionists, journalists, community workers, sociologists, actors, musicians, and artists. Some of the discussions and presentations were influenced by ideas derived from Steiner's concepts of a threefold social organism (which itself could be related to the threefold structures of the human being described above) characterized by three independently functioning social organs: a free cultural and educational life, a democratic equality of human rights, and a new associative and cooperative economics. One key idea introduced by Beuys from Steiner's economic theory involved a dynamic understanding of economics, whereby the healthy, cyclical flow of money (or capital) through society was compared with the circulation of blood in the human body (and, obviously, connected with the circulation imagery of the honey pump as well).

In this connection, Beuys's *Honey Pump* pointed to another of his creative uses of Steiner's lectures on bees—namely, to reference aspects of the structure of the bee colony for a more harmonious human social life, for "social sculpture." In the lecture excerpts in the appendix from September 29, 1905, and April 21, 1909, Steiner portrays the group soul of the bee-hive with its capacity for work-oriented social cooperation as a condition that human beings will be able to achieve only in the distant future. Beuys once spoke of the bee cult as an

> ... allusion to socialism as practiced in the big watch-making cooperatives of the Republic of the Bees at La Chaux-de-Fonds. There you can still see many sculptures of bees on the walls and foundations, as symbols of socialism. This does not mean mechanistic state socialism, but a socialist organism in which all parts function as in a living body. In physiological terms this is not hierarchical: the queen bee's place lies between

head and heart, and the drones become the cells which are constantly renewed. The whole builds a unity which has to function perfectly, but in a humane warm way through principles of cooperation and brotherhood.[40]

Bakunin, Marx, and Maeterlinck had all drawn similar analogies. Yet Beuys was clear that a colony of bees differs significantly from human society because it is not composed of independent individuals. "The bee is one cell in the whole organism, just like a skin cell or a muscle cell or a blood cell. The best analogy is with the blood cells that swarm through the whole body." "Seen that way, my body is also a perfectly functioning state."[41] Thus, Beuys championed Steiner's ideal of a social *organism* that would be threefold in structure like the human being.

For Beuys, the whole point of *Honey Pump* was its integration with the human beings participating in the Free International University events. These discussions on solving social problems—not the elaborate physical apparatus—were the real *Honey Pump* as far as he was concerned.[42] By reference to a 1974 postcard "multiple" artwork, as well as a diagram drawn by Beuys during a 1975 interview with Jean-Pierre Van Tieghem, both titled *Honey Is Flowing in All Directions*, we may conclude that Beuys used honey for the social warmth forces of its origin in the bee colony, forces that he hoped would help dissolve or resolve hardened dualisms in modern humanity's worldview and achieve a "real human implosion" that could renew western civilization and advance human spiritual evolution. In the interview diagram, he mentions the dualisms of subject and object, body and spirit, perception

40. Tisdale, *Joseph Beuys*, p. 44.
41. Quoted in Stachelhaus, *Joseph Beuys*, p. 58.
42. As he relates in Harlan, *Joseph Beuys*, p. 59.

and conception.[43] Beuys's primary purpose was ultimately to stimulate social and spiritual reform, and, in addition to his political endeavors, he turned to innovative contemporary art forms as his means for conveying this message in a way that would reach people more deeply than purely intellectual proposals and, hopefully, motivate them to creatively get involved in changing themselves and their world. Rather than an attempt to create yet another formal innovation within the ivory tower of avant garde art, this call to reform is the meaning, justification, and potential of his social sculpture and its associated dictum: Everyone is an artist. Although he was several times disappointed by attempts at political reform, Beuys never lost faith in art as "the sole, revolutionary force capable of transforming the earth, humanity, the social order...."[44]

David Adams, Ph.D.
Penn Valley, California, 1998

DAVID ADAMS holds a Ph.D in art history education and has taught art history at state universities and art schools for eight years. He has written numerous published articles, essays, and art exhibition booklets. He is currently an adjunct faculty in art history at Sierra College, director of the Center for Architecture & Design Research, and a freelance writer and editor.

43. *Joseph Beuys* (Brussels and Paris: Galerie Isy Brachot, 1990).
44. Kuoni, ed., *Energy Plan*, p. 99.

• Index

A

alcohol, as stimulating the I, 111
allergy to bees, 67
anger, bees' reaction to, 59–60
ant acid, 148
ant colonies, 123–24
  as controlling mold, 138
  thinking of, 137
"ant eggs," 125
ant juice, 131–32
anthill construction, 170
ants, 25–27, 115–17
  agricultural, as farmers, 124,
    136–37, 144
  contrasted with bees, 2, 3
  group soul of, 176
  nest building, 117–24
  role in nature, 133
aphids, 118–19
apiculture, 16
arthritis. See rheumatism
artificial methods. See under bee-
    keeping; breeding; feeding;
    sugar
astral body, 106
astrology, 62, 81–82. See also Sun;
    Venus
  nectar growth and, 62, 63

B

bee poison. See poison
bee society, natural wisdom of,
    20
beehive
  cosmic and environmental influ-
    ences on, 1
  group soul of, 176
  human beings compared with,
    106
  as incomplete human being, 157
  learning by emersing conscious-
    ness into, 170
  life within, 170
  as single entity, 115
  spiritual influence on, 177
beekeeper, death of
  impact on bees, 56, 66–67, 69,
    185
beekeeper-bee relationship, 185
  spiritual bond, 56
beekeeping
  artificial methods in, 75. See also
    under breeding; feeding
  instinctual, 85
  occupation of, 76–78
bee-like insects, 115. See also ants;
    wasps

bees. *See also specific topics*
knowledge of how to help themselves, 72
as sacred, 22
types of, 76, 89. *See also* queen
bee; wood bees
Sun development phase and, 8
beeswax
candles from, 22
blood, human
compared with swarming bee
horde, 68
as driven by the I, 106
blood flow, influence of movement and I-organization on,
108
blood juice in bees, 86–87
blossoms, how workers find, 12–
13. *See also* flowers
breeding, artificial, 20–21, 72
detrimental effects on bonding,
21
interference with queen-worker
relationship, 21
of queen bees, 177

C
carbon dioxide, 149
caterpillars, 124–25
cells. *See also* honeycomb
characteristics, 51
construction of, 7
crystals compared with, 50–51
differentiation of types of, 7
ingeniously shaped, 7
Christmas trees, 158–59
clairvoyance, 14
clover, 89
clover acid, 148

color vision, 24–28
consciousness, types of, 169–170
cooperation, 2
crossbreeding, of honeybees from
fig wasps, 179
crystals, quartz, 48–50, 181–82
milk as analogous to, 52, 53
wax cells as analogous to, 50–
53

D
death, animal. *See also* beekeeper,
death of
continuation of group soul after,
172–73
deficiencies, as calling forth
opposing power, 20
disease. *See specific diseases*
Dollinger, Mr., 83
drones
as "Earth" creatures, 104, 105
Earth developmental phase and,
9, 10
fertilization capability, 10
as traitors who have fallen to
Earth, 10
dying individuals, formic acid
production in, 156

E
Earth
influence on bees, 104
resuscitated via formic acid, 154
soul and spirit of
formic acid as basis of, 155
seasons and, 154
Earth *vs.* Sun influences, 13
eggs. *See also under* wasps; workers
ant, 125

deposition of, 100, 103
emotions, 60
  human, six-sided balance and,
    59–60
Emrich, Dr. Paula, 40
Erbsmehl, Mr., 65, 66, 75, 83
etheric aura of swarm, 175
etheric body, 106
  of plant leaf, 180
etheric powers, 179
etheric world, 180
evolution, stages of, 170

F
familiarity and recognition, 68–
  69
fear, bees' reaction to, 59–60
feeding, artificial, 37, 73
  compared with forcefeeding,
    115
fertilization, 103, 105
  aversion to, 104
  as contact between embryo's
    heavenly and earthly ele-
    ments, 105
  as dependent upon weather, 104
  drones' capability for, 10
  excessive drone birth due to
    improper, 114
  needed for same-sex reproduc-
    tion, 11
  as public event, 11
  queen's relationship with Sun
    and, 11
  role of Sun and Earth in, 104
figs and fig trees, 95–97, 99–100,
  183
flower blossoms, bee's etheric aura
  during contact with, 174–75

flowers. *See also* honey
  bees as robbing honey from,
    126–27
  bees' attraction to, 87, 88
  experience of bees, 126–27
  need for bee-like insects, 134,
    137
  relationship with bee-like
    insects, 103, 119, 133–34
formic acid, 133–37
  allows Earth's resuscitation,
    154
  created from oxalic acid, 150–
    52, 154
  seasons and, 156
  as foundation of soul and spirit,
    153, 155
  in humans, 144–45, 149
  deficiency, 146, 154
  needed throughout nature,
    132
  omnipresence, 150–51, 155
  purulent infections overcome by,
    154
  self-created *vs.* artificial, 147–48
  soul element of, 152, 154
foul brood, 101–2

G
galls. *See* wasps, gall
gastric juice in bees, 86–87
gout, 132
  treatment of, 108, 110
  weak I-organization as cause of,
    108
greenhouse plants, 87, 88
group souls, animals, 172–73,
  176
group-self, human I as, 172

H
Hahn, R., 101–2, 178
heart disease, 110–11
  bee poison treatment, 109, 111
  as malfunction of I-organiza-
    tion, 105
hexagonal cells, 17
hexagonal house, 7
homeopathic medicines, 37–39
honey. *See also* flowers
  enlightenment from, 3–4
  negative physiological reactions
    to, 79–80
  powers of, 177
  produced by bee out of its own
    body, 141
  as regurgitated bee product,
    12
  as soul sharing, 4
  therapeutic and nutritional qual-
    ities, 18–19, 40–42, 45–47,
    51–55, 91, 129
  body solidified by, 19
  derived from plant nectar,
    20
  transformation of other foods
    into, 38
honeycombs, 6. *See also* cells
  construction of, 100
  eating, 83–84
hornets, 67, 72
  nest inside hive, 73
horses, 59
human body. *See also* human
    physiology
  consciousness of each organ,
    169
  muscle, 17, 69
  power of glycerin in, 149

rotting wood compared with,
    152–53
human culture, as too brain-ori-
    ented, 138
human fear, bees' reaction to,
    59
human I, as group-self, 172
human physiology
  anthill compared with, 144–45
  beehive compared with, 16–18
  blood cells as workers, 16, 17
  body as honeycomb, 17
  cerebral neurons as drones, 16
  head as beehive, 18
  muscle cells as wax cells, 17
  protein cells as queen bee,
    16
humans
  bees as helpful *vs.* harmful to,
    126–27
  bees' reaction to, 60
  four parts of, 105–6
  as microcosms, 150, 155
  old age in, 153

I
I-being(s), 106
  animal, 172
  as moving and controlling
    blood, 106
immunization to bee poison,
    112–13
infections
  astral body's role in, 154
  overcome by formic acid, 154
infrared light, 26, 30
insect hordes, spiritual connec-
    tion with content of plants,
    140

insects. *See specific insects*
instinct, 121–22

J
juniper, 158–59

L
larva, 7
lemurs, 175
life, maintenance of, 137
light
  chemical effects of, 34–35
  electric, bees' reactions to, 80–81
  infrared, 26, 30
  ultraviolet, 25–29
  young queen bee as giving off, 156
love
  group *vs.* individual, 3
  life based on, 3
  throughout bee colony, 2
love life, element of soul in, 2

M
maggot. *See* larva
maturity, time needed to reach, 8
medicine, 109–10
  poisons compared with, 107
milk
  crystals as analogous to, 52, 53
  nutritional value, 42–44, 47, 55, 129–30
    integrated six-dimensional effect of, 52–53
  powers of, 177
mother bee, protection of young, 143
mousetrap, 30
  Venus flytrap compared with, 28

Müller, Mr. (beekeeper), 5, 7, 12, 21, 23, 31–33, 37, 56–57, 65–67, 72, 75, 83, 86, 88, 113, 177
muscle, bee *vs.* human, 69

N
nature
  bees' role in, 133
  inner workings revealed by insect activity, 140–41
  wisdom of, 20, 142–44
    dangers of intruding upon, 20
nectar, collection of, 5
nest building
  ant, 117–24
  hornet, 73
  wisdom in, 142–44

O
organs. *See* human physiology
out-of-body experiences, 107
oxalic acid, 148–51

P
parthogenesis (virgin brood), 11, 33–34
  can only produce drones (opposite sex), 11
perfection, bee's achieving, 141
perspiration, 67
plant leaf, etheric body of, 180
plant nectar, honey's therapeutic qualities as derived from, 20
planthood, evolutionary period of, 130–31
plants
  greenhouse, 87, 88
  reactions to specific persons, 61

spiritual connection insect
  hordes, 140
poison. *See also* formic acid
  bee's need for, 106
  death prevented by, 137
  effects on animals, 133
  effects on humans, 132
  healing powers, 107–11, 134–
    35, 144
    prevention of death, 137
  the I as present in, 106
  immunity to, 112
  as life sustaining, 135, 137–38
  medicines compared with, 107
  replenishing of, 137–38
  as strengthening the I, 107, 108
  Sun takes away power of, 15
  twilight caused by, 15
  of wasp, as partially transformed
    formic acid, 151
pollen, removal and collection, 6
prussic acid, 29

Q
queen bees. *See also* parthogenesis
  artificial breeding, 177
  birth, 13–15
  experienced as phosphorescent
    source, 30
  inferior, 113
    giving birth to all drones, 113
  old
    departure of compared with
      spirit leaving body, 156–57
    leaves when young queen
      appears, 32
  pseudo, 114
  separates to remain under Sun
    influences, 15

time needed for maturation, 8
Sun phase and, 8–10
young
  bees awakened by emergence
    of, 156
  as giving off light, 156
  as "glowworm," 32
  take away power of old queen's
    poison, 156

R
reincarnation, 155–57
repression, sexual, 2
reproduction. *See* fertilization
rheumatism, 132
  abated bee or wasp sting, 105
  treatment, 108–11
  weak I-organization as cause of,
    108
rickets, alleviated by honey, 19

S
seasons, spirit of Earth and, 154
sense, midway between smell and
  taste, 27
sexual repression, 2
sexuality, 2, 171
  as completely chemical, 34
  dominance of queen bees, 2
  renounced in service of hive's
    love life, 3
shortages, opposing power called
  forth by, 20
silicic acid, 51–54, 182
sleep, departure from physical
  body during, 107
smell, 27
  knowledge obtained through
    special sense of, 138

sense of, 36
soul, 2–3
space, efficient use of, 7
spiritual beings, elemental
 formation of, 171–72
 in real world, 171, 173
stinging, 14. *See also* poison
 as defense against foreign influence, 15
 effects of, 110–11
  seeing rainbow colors, 110–11
 elicited by human anger, 56, 60
 resistance to, 111
sugar
 artificial application of, 113
 fed to bees, 37, 113
 fed to horse
  elicits loving relationship, 59
Sun
 bees' attunement with, 103
 influence on bees, 103–4
 nectar growth influenced by,
  62–63
 poison's power taken away by, 15
 queen bee and, 8–11
 role in fertilization, 104
 swarming due to influence of,
  14
 workers and, 10, 104
Sun animals, bees as, 81
Sun phases
 queen bee maturation and, 8–10
 types of bees and, 8
Sun *vs.* Earth influences, 13
swarm
 compared with human soul,
  156
 etheric aura of, 175
 fear of lack of poison, 156

 as trying to find way into spiritual world, 157
swarming, 31–32
 caused by new influence of Sun,
  14
 as going on strike, 32–33
 premature, 33
sylphs, 175

T
Tartarus remedy, 108
taste, 27
trees. *See* figs and fig trees
twilight, living in continual, 15

U
ultraviolet light, 25–29
unity, desire for, 157
uric acid, 102, 180

V
Venus, 2, 170–71
Venus consciousness, 170–71
Venus cycle, 178
Venus flytrap compared with
  mousetrap, 28
vision, 30. *See also* color vision;
  queen bee

W
wasps, 92–93, 98, 115–17, 131
 contrasted with bees, 1–3
 cynipidae, 93
 eggs of, 180, 183
 figs and, 183
 gall, 93–94, 134, 180
 honeycomb building, 115–18
 laying of eggs, 93–98
  in caterpillar, 125

poison of, 108
role in nature, 133
weather, 61–62
wisdom, 2–3
wood bees, 142, 153, 159–60
workers
  behavior after reaching maturity,
    12–13
  blood cells compared with, 16, 17
  changed into egg-laying queen,
    114
  clairvoyance, 14
  laying of eggs by, 114

  as Sun and Earth creature, 104
  under Sun's influence, 10

During the last two decades of the nineteenth century Austrian-born Rudolf Steiner (1861–1925) became a respected and well-published scientific, literary, and philosophical scholar, particularly known for his work on Goethe's scientific writings. After the turn of the century he began to develop his earlier philosophical principles into an approach to methodical research of psychological and spiritual phenomena.

His multifaceted genius has led to innovative and holistic approaches in medicine, philosophy, religion, education (Waldorf schools), special education, economics, agriculture (Biodynamic method), science, architecture, drama, the new arts of speech and eurythmy, and other fields of activity. In 1924 he founded the General Anthroposophical Society, which today has branches throughout the world.